R

D1632392

18604

TO BE
DISPOSED
BY
AUTHORITY

NELSON'S AGRICULTURE SERIES

GENERAL EDITORS :

SIR WILLIAM G. OGG M.A. PH.D. AND G. V. JACKS M.A. B.SC.

BRITISH FARMING
1939-49

BRITISH FARMING
1939-49

EDITH H. WHETHAM

Gilbey Lecturer in the History and Economics of Agriculture,
School of Agriculture, Cambridge University

THOMAS NELSON AND SONS LTD
LONDON EDINBURGH PARIS MELBOURNE
TORONTO AND NEW YORK

THOMAS NELSON AND SONS LTD
Parkside Works Edinburgh 9
3 Henrietta Street London WC2
312 Flinders Street Melbourne C1
5 Parker's Buildings Burg Street Cape Town

THOMAS NELSON AND SONS (CANADA) LTD
91–93 Wellington Street West   Toronto 1

THOMAS NELSON AND SONS
19 East 47th Street New York 17

SOCIÉTÉ FRANÇAISE D'EDITIONS NELSON
25 rue Henri Barbusse Paris V[e]

———

First published 1952

PREFACE

THE purpose of this book is to provide a brief history of British farming in the decade of the Second World War. Contemporary history is the most difficult to study and the hardest to write. Events of past centuries are recorded in standard text books with their consequences described and assessed, but the events of the past few years have to be disentangled from articles written by specialists for experts, from the records of Parliamentary debates and from the pronouncements of Ministers and officials. Some of the details are still hidden in the records of Government Departments, while controversies provoked by war-time action still echo in the post-war world. We do not know how temporary or permanent our post-war troubles may prove to have been, and we cannot therefore make a final judgment on the wisdom of the actions taken to deal with them.

Yet the attempt to write this short history of farming seemed justified by the great economic and administrative changes which took place between 1939 and 1949. The agriculture that emerged in 1945 from the nightmare of war was strikingly different from that which in September 1939 answered the call to action stations ; an account, though necessarily provisional, of these changes may have a useful part to play. Those studying for agricultural degrees, and agricultural scientists and administrators who want to know something of the economic structure of farming, may find it convenient to have in one volume an account of what happened in the last decade and why it happened.

This book is in some respects a supplement to two others recently published—that by Dr Orwin, *A History of English Farming*, which covers 600 years on a masterly canvas ; and that by Professor Thomas, *An Introduction to Agricultural Economics*. I hope my contribution to agricultural history may be judged not unworthy to stand on the shelf beside those of Dr Orwin and Professor Thomas, in the line that leads back through Hall and Ernle and Caird to William Cobbett and Arthur Young, who also wrote of farming under the impact of a world war.

From 1942 to 1947 I was engaged in the Civil Histories Section of the Cabinet Offices in compiling a narrative of food production in the Second World War. I relinquished that official work shortly after returning to Cambridge, and this entirely unofficial account is based only on published material.

My thanks for generous help with this book are due to the late Dr Menzies-Kitchin and to Professor Sir Frank Engledow, of the Cambridge School of Agriculture; to Professor Nash of Aberystwyth; and to Miss Cohen of Newnham College, Cambridge. In my official duties I incurred a heavy obligation to many Civil Servants who gave freely of their time and memories; I hope this record may convey to them my gratitude for their assistance.

E. H. W.

School of Agriculture,
Cambridge 1952

CONTENTS

CHAPTER I

BRITISH FARMING, 1919-39

THE agricultural revolution of the nineteen-forties sprang from two compulsions—the economic structure of British farming as it had evolved in the twenty years from 1919 to 1939 ; and the needs of a war which, beginning on the frontier between Germany and Poland, engulfed the world. A history of agriculture over this decade must begin therefore with a brief account firstly of its development between the wars and secondly of the plans made for its conversion to a war-time footing.

The Farms

In 1938 a total of 440,000 agricultural holdings were recorded in Great Britain, but not all of these were farms in the usual sense. Many of the smaller units were cultivated in conjunction with other land ; some ' holdings ' consisted of land in rough pasture used by other industries than farming. Information collected during the Second World War indicates that, at its start, there were probably some 350,000 farms in Britain, together with an uncertain number of agricultural holdings less than 5 acres in size.

Most of these farms were family businesses, run by the farmer and his wife, sometimes alone and sometimes with one or two helpers who were often members of the family. Barely 3 per cent of the farms over 5 acres in size in England and Wales employed ten men or more in 1941 ; two-thirds of them employed either none or only one regular hired worker. On most farms the occupier bought and sold, kept the accounts and records, planned the cropping and stocking, organised the routine of the other workers, coped with emergencies and Bank Holidays, and was himself responsible for much of the manual work in field and farmyard. Only a minority of farms were so large that the farmer could be fully employed in marketing and organising, could be, in fact, a manager, as that term is usually understood in industry.

Indeed one of the most striking facts about British farming was the wide range in the size of the farm business and in the amount of tenants' capital. There was great variation in the educational and social standing of the farmers, in their knowledge of the sciences behind the daily routine and in their willingness to use the technical facilities provided for farming by the Agricultural Departments and the County Councils. Britain exported pedigree livestock to many countries, yet the stock kept on the majority of farms was unsatisfactory in breeding and performance. The scientific institutes, such as those at Rothamsted, Cambridge, Edinburgh and Aberystwyth, drew visitors from all over the world, but only a small proportion of British farmers visited their demonstrations or read their publications. Traditional practices, modified only by economic necessity, were followed on thousands of farms in the crop rotations first developed 150 years ago after the introduction of turnips and sown grasses.

The Economic Trends

The twenty years and ten months between the Armistice of November 1918 and the outbreak of war in September 1939 was generally an unprofitable period for British farmers. Profits had come too easily during the sharp rise in prices between 1914 and 1917 ; the measures of price control and of food rationing introduced in 1917 did not long survive the Armistice, and the price rise was renewed in the early months of 1919. In a modified form the Agriculture Act, 1920, continued for wheat and oats the guaranteed prices which had stimulated the war-time ploughing campaign, but the security thus offered for the post-war years was not to be achieved. From May 1920 the general level of wholesale prices began to fall, and fell for eighteen months to reach a level barely half of that recorded at the peak. Linked to world markets by its sales, as well as by its purchases of feedingstuffs, fertilisers and petrol, British agriculture shared with other industries the disastrous results of this general price fall. The Agriculture Act was repealed when the Government realised the financial cost to the Exchequer of paying, even for two products, prices related to the ' ascertained average costs of production ' incurred at levels ruling six to eighteen months previous. But the cost had to be borne by millions of farmers in Britain and elsewhere, not only for cereals (whose prices fell more sharply than most) but to a lesser extent for livestock products also.

British farmers were thus left unassisted to cope with the enlarged arable acreage which had been called into being by the threat of famine in 1917 and 1918. Although wages for farm workers fell rapidly from 1920 to 1924, they declined less than the prices of farm products ; and in 1924 the Wages Board Act revived the war-time organisation for fixing a minimum wage in each county of England and Wales. (Similar legislation for Scotland was delayed until 1937.) The higher cost of labour to the farmer stimulated those types of farming which gave a high return per man employed —dairying, intensive production of pigs, eggs or vegetables, together with mechanised grain growing on easily worked soils. The mixed family farm also proved its survival value ; at the expense of a low standard of living, the unit could outlast temporary fluctuations in prices. But this precarious balance achieved between 1924 and 1929 was again undermined by the renewed fall in cereal prices which heralded the Great Depression. The farms with substantial sales of grain were the first to be affected, particularly those on heavy soils where cultivations and field drainage were costly. On cheap feedingstuffs livestock enterprises flourished for a time, until falling demand and increasing supplies affected those prices as well. The index of the prices of farm crops compiled by the Ministry of Agriculture sank from $106\frac{1}{2}$ (1927–9 = 100) in 1928 to $73\frac{1}{2}$ in 1930, and to $70\frac{1}{2}$ in 1933 ; the prices of livestock and livestock products (on the same base period) showed little change in 1929 and 1930, but fell sharply in subsequent years to $74\frac{1}{2}$ in 1933.

The gradual recovery of agricultural profits from 1932

onwards was aided by various measures described below, and also by the general recovery in world prices. The depression brought considerable changes in the structure of British agriculture which adjusted itself to produce a larger quantity of the more profitable foods—livestock products and vegetables ; its output valued at 1927–9 prices increased by some 15 per cent between 1928–9 and 1936–7. Yet in the ten years before the Second World War, the number of regular workers employed in agriculture in Great Britain fell from 745,000 to 600,800, or by 20 per cent ; the fall was proportionately largest for women and for youths. The pull of competing employments, offering higher wages, shorter hours and better housing, and the push of farm mechanisation combined to reduce the numbers employed on the land while raising output per man. Tractors—the war-babies of 1917–19 —became general in arable districts ; combine harvesters, crop sprayers, milking machines, row-crop cultivators and a host of other labour-saving devices were tried, modified and adopted by a few progressive farmers. Milk recording, improved strains of crops, bull licensing to eliminate the worst animals, more accurate knowledge of soils and manuring, and the prevention of disease and pests, all led to lower costs and a higher output per man.

Such prosperity as was thus attained was based largely on livestock and their products. Milk, cattle, pigs, poultry and eggs were, in that order, the most important sources of farm income and probably of farm profits also. Sales of milk in Great Britain were valued at £68 millions in 1937–8 ; potatoes, the most valuable farm crop, brought some £14½ millions, while sales of wheat totalled £9 millions, including subsidy. In the autumn of 1938 there were about 110,000 milk producers registered under the Milk Marketing Boards, which did not cover Northern Ireland nor the whole of Scotland ; in comparison, some 76,650 farmers in the United Kingdom were registered as growers of wheat. Cheap feedingstuffs were of primary importance to the dairy farmer, to the specialist producer of pigs and eggs and to a lesser extent to the grazier who sold fat cattle. Even in the predominantly arable districts, the tendency in the inter-war years was to increase the output of livestock products by the greater use of purchased feedingstuffs, and to devote the fields to cash crops such as wheat, barley, potatoes, sugar beet and vegetables rather than to the production of fodder crops. The decline in the area of tillage [1] was relatively least in Scotland and in the old arable districts of the east and north-east of England ; it was relatively greatest in the other areas where, even before 1914, crops had been less important. ' Mixed ' farming —arable cultivation with a cycle of corn, root crops and leys of grass or clover—gave way over much of England and Wales to other types of farming. In the west and midlands there was the all-grass dairy or stock farm ; open-air dairying with moveable milking sheds was adopted on the dry chalk uplands of southern England, where cows were fed on cattle-cake and grass ; in eastern districts milk production was increasingly combined with sugar beet and other crops for sale. The all-grass farm lost the machinery and traditions of cultivation ; its land, though acquiring fertility from cake-fed animals, tended to become ' cow-sick ' and to deteriorate in feeding value. The outlying or intractable fields of arable farms were apt to follow the same trend and to become indifferent grass or to lie derelict.

Near urban areas there was a development of ' processing ' farms, keeping one type of stock—cows, pigs or hens—on purchased feeds. In times of cheap feedingstuffs, these holdings were often profitable, though their prosperity was precariously balanced between a rise in cereal prices and an outbreak of disease. In the southern counties of Scotland, the relative unprofitability of corn production led to an extension in the area of permanent pasture used mainly for milk production. In the more severe climate of the north and east, the fall in arable was comparatively small, but even in these districts farmers tended to lengthen the duration of their leys, and to use the extra area of temporary grass for flocks of sheep. Here, as in the midland grazings of England, it was

---

[1] Tillage is land under crops and bare fallow ; arable is land under crops, bare fallow and temporary grass.

the fall in cattle and sheep prices from 1931 to 1935 and again in 1938 that most affected farm incomes.

The Inter-war Depression

Much has been written and said about the causes and results of these two agricultural depressions of the inter-war years. Two such points may be noted here. The armistice of 1918 meant that sooner or later the huge corn production would have to be adjusted to the normal demand for a more varied and more nutritious diet. But because of the prevailing economic thought and political feeling, the State did little to help with this painful task of re-adjustment ; and the general deflation in world prices from 1920 intensified the difficulties of the process. It is true that agriculture was not the only sufferer ; the other war-inflated industries—shipbuilding, the merchant navy, the iron and steel trades—were also left unaided to struggle with similar problems of excess capacity and unbalanced structure. But there are peculiar features in the economy of agriculture which aggravated its difficulties and which also intensified the effects of the economic depression of 1929–33 :

‘ On a prosperous farm a good deal of the annual expenditure is incurred on the maintenance of farm buildings, and equipment, particularly hedges, ditches and drains. In a time of depression, the farmer can, and often does, effect temporary economies by neglecting this work, and by similar activities such as cutting down his stock (and thus depleting fertility), over-cropping land which ought to be rested, neglecting cultivations and so on. In short, he can live on his capital. Since the full effect of this type of neglect is not felt for several years, he can carry on in this way for some time. If the depression is not a serious one, or he was fairly well equipped to withstand it, he may, when the better times come, be able to recover lost ground and carry on as before ; but there will be some individuals of meagre resources who will run heavily into debt, seriously impair the productivity of their holdings and reach a stage in which they have either to relinquish their impoverished farms to new occupiers or to spend many years of struggle on a subsistence level— generally the latter. The tenacity of the farmer in hanging on to his farm at all costs is thus apt to result in a chronic local condition of undercapitalisation in agriculture. The effect is enhanced by the optimism of new entrants who frequently take over a holding with insufficient capital in the hope of being able to make enough profits to put back into the business to restore the farm to proper condition. Even in prosperous times there will be a marginal fringe of farmers, and therefore, of farms, in such conditions ; and when there is a series of depressions or the structure of agriculture is undergoing secular changes the number may be very considerable. When this kind of thing happens in industry the impoverished units usually drop out and their remaining business is absorbed by other enterprises ; but impoverished pieces of land are not readily absorbed and thus local agricultural impoverishment, sometimes acute, is always chronic.

'In the last twenty years there has, I believe, been a tendency for agricultural impoverishment in this country to increase. The effect has not been, however, to result in derelict farms so much as in derelict fields. In certain hard-hit areas farmers have been pushed to the extreme and have deliberately allowed part of their holdings—the more outlying or less fertile fields—to fall out of cultivation in order to concentrate their limited resources on the remainder. The depressed agricultural areas of Britain are not composed of derelict farms—though such exist—but of impoverished farms with derelict fields, and the problem of dealing with them is thereby made more difficult.' [1]

Two types of farming in particular were especially affected by this chronic lack of capital. The first was arable farming on heavy and intractable soils, such as the ' wheat

[1] Kendall, M. J., ' The Financing of British Agriculture,' *Journal of the Royal Statistical Society*, vol. civ, Part ii, 1941

and bean ' lands of Essex, Huntingdon and other counties. These soils demand expensive maintenance work on drainage, cultivation and fertilisers ; until the advent of crawler tractors there was often little choice between a rigid rotation of wheat, beans and fallow, and indifferent pasture. The high costs of cultivations and the fall in cereal prices squeezed out the working capital of many farmers in these districts ; after a certain degree of neglect, the cost of reclamation, including perhaps heavy arrears of drainage work, outweighed any possible income to be derived from current prices. Another rigid structure is hill sheep farming, whose output is limited by climate, altitude and poor soil to wool and store stock. In the ten years after the First World War there was a brisk trade in breeding ewes while lowland flocks were rebuilt, but after 1930 these hill farms seldom provided more than a bare living for their operators. Their slow maturing cattle and three-year-old wethers became unpopular with consumers who preferred the smaller joints from lowland lambs and baby beeves. In Wales the wether flock practically disappeared, but the denser stocking of the hills with breeding ewes and their lambs led to further problems—an increased drain on the mineral content of the soil, the spread of bracken and an increase in disease. In many areas of Scotland even this limited adjustment was prohibited by the more severe climate, and there was a steady fall in the sheep and cattle maintained in the Highlands. The widely fluctuating but generally low prices obtained for their products in the last ten years before the Second World War thus intensified the deterioration in these farms and in their low standards of housing and equipment.

Another cause of much local impoverishment must also be noted. The high cost of building repairs and the rising standards for cowsheds, piggeries and water supplies absorbed a much higher proportion of the rent than in the early years of the twentieth century ; some landlords and many owner-occupiers were unable to maintain the existing buildings, let alone to improve them. The sale of many large estates, to pay duties on the death of their former owners, often forced farmers to purchase their holdings ; the fall in prices from 1920–3 and again from 1929 left them burdened with interest and mortgage charges.

There were therefore ' depressed areas ' in British farming ; there were impoverished farms and many derelict fields.　Of these much was heard ; farmers who were not making profits took care that the Government and the tax-payer should know the fact.　Less was heard from those who made a modest living from dairying, or from judicious blend of mechanised cropping with livestock production.　But undoubtedly the average income obtained by the agricultural worker and by the family farm in the inter-war years remained low relative to that secured by the corresponding urban classes in times of regular employment.　In this small and overcrowded island, it was this unfavourable contrast which was so resented by farmers and farm workers.　Memories of high profits easily earned in the last war and the experience of losses inflicted by the two subsequent deflations increased this resentment against that entity ' the Government ' to whose misdeeds was ascribed every evil besetting the farmer.

This mistrust towards the State was an unfortunate legacy of the methods by which economic changes had been effected, rather than of those changes themselves, many of which benefited both the farmer and his customers.　There is no reason to deplore the steady increase in demand for milk, eggs and vegetables and the falling consumption of bread, all signs of a rising standard of life and of a better diet. The shift in emphasis required from agriculture by these slow changes in demand was within the technical capacity of most types of farming.　The mechanisation of many farm processes raised the efficiency of the worker, enabled him slowly to improve his earning power and to escape from much back-breaking drudgery.　Even as a basis for war production these agricultural changes were not all unfavourable.　The increasing import of feedingstuffs supplied to the soil huge quantities of fertilising elements which could be brought into action by the use of the plough ; it was calculated that, on the average of the three pre-war years, the effective manurial residues of imported feedingstuffs supplied from one- to two-thirds as much nitrogen, potash and phosphoric acid as was obtained by the direct application of fertilisers. The decline in arable was not so serious a matter as it would have been a quarter of a century earlier ; the modern tractor enormously facilitated the rapid conversion of grass to ploughland, and extra tractors could be supplied more speedily than extra horses. Still, the lack of cultivating tools and of the knowledge how to use them was in many districts a real handicap at the start of a food-production campaign ; the financial and psychological legacy of two price deflations had left agriculture short of working capital and embittered its relations with the State.

Some of the quantitative aspects of the changes described so briefly in the preceding paragraphs can be traced in the annual agricultural statistics. Between 1914 and 1939 the area of cultivated land—that under crops and grass—in Great Britain had fallen by some $2\frac{3}{4}$ million acres. Two million acres were lost under roads or rough grazing, and the remaining $\frac{3}{4}$ million can be accounted for by urban development and by the demands of the military services, which had taken nearly 150,000 acres of agricultural land in the nineteen-thirties. The area under corn crops and fodder roots fell between 1914 and 1939 by $2\frac{1}{2}$ million acres while that under pasture was little changed. Sugar-beet became an established crop in eastern districts and more vegetables were grown on farms in every area. The number of cows and heifers increased by some 700,000 and there were a million more pigs. Sheep numbers fluctuated widely during this quarter of a century ; the main trend was a decline in folded sheep kept on arable farms and an increase in grassland flocks ; total numbers were little changed on the average of years, but the geographical distribution was appreciably altered.

AGRICULTURE AND THE STATE

Shortly before the First World War the State began to finance and to develop the provision of technical advice to farmers and of scientific research into agricultural problems. By

1939 a triple structure had been erected, at whose apex was the Agricultural Research Council, co-ordinating the research at the specialised institutes and agricultural colleges. At eleven provincial centres (most of them connected with a university) the Ministry of Agriculture had a staff of scientists and economists to advise on local problems of technique and farm management ; this organisation also collected valuable information on the finances of different types of farming and particularly of milk production. In Scotland similar facilities were provided at the three agricultural colleges in Edinburgh, Glasgow and Aberdeen. At another level, the county councils in England and Wales also maintained an agricultural staff, engaged partly on advisory work, partly in teaching at the farm institutes and partly on the administration of the small-holding estates owned by the county councils. For no other industry did the tax-payers and rate-payers provide such facilities for research and advice on technical matters, and it was all the more unfortunate that so few farmers took advantage of them. It must be admitted that the structure lacked cohesion between its parts as well as lacking contact with the great mass of farmers. The number of the agricultural staff employed by the county councils varied with the financial resources of those bodies ; therefore, although the Ministry provided some grants in aid, the rural counties where agriculture was the main occupation tended to have fewer facilities than areas which included industrial or residential districts. But in spite of imperfections this organisation was an enormous help to administrators in the early days of the Second World War ; in every county there were men trained in agricultural science with a knowledge of local farmers, of local soils and of local problems.

This permanent but inconspicuous assistance for farmers was overshadowed in the pre-war decade by a variety of measures born of the Great Depression and aimed at the alleviation of its worst effects on British agriculture. They can be classified under three heads, (1) the restriction of supplies, (2) the provision of direct subsidies for certain commodities, and (3) the organisation of the processes of marketing.

(1) Restriction of Imports

The restriction of imports was designed to offset one much publicised result of the Great Depression which showed itself in all countries as a failure of demand to absorb current production at customary prices. Confronted with falling demand, unremunerative prices and an agricultural output which tended to increase rather than to decline, exporting countries increased the volume of their food supplies to this country, then the largest free market for agricultural products of all kinds. The National Government, returned in the general election of 1931, declared its intention of restricting imports so as to secure, firstly, some stability in total supplies and in prices, and secondly, a larger share in the home market for the British farmer. Moderate import duties were imposed on many foods from foreign countries, though supplies from the Empire were generally exempt. Direct quantitative restrictions (quotas) were imposed on the imports of bacon, beef, pork, mutton, tinned and processed milks. The total effect of these measures was to restrict severely the imports from foreign countries, to allow a certain expansion in imports from the Empire and thus to reduce total imports somewhat below the level reached in the early years of the depression.

Critics were quick to point out that restricting imports by quotas might compel the British consumer to pay a higher price for the foreign product, without giving a corresponding advantage to the British farmer. This was especially so for bacon, imports of which were progressively reduced from 1932 onwards in order to permit an expansion in home supplies without exceeding a total annual supply of 10,700,000 cwt. The margin in price formerly obtained by the best types of British bacon over the imported product was substantially narrowed after 1934, while the British consumer paid a larger total sum for a smaller quantity of Danish bacon. There was in fact a strong consumer preference for Danish bacon, so that many housewives were prepared to make do with a smaller quantity of their accustomed brand rather than to buy the unfamiliar British product.

Another indirect result of these quotas was to encourage producers, both in this country and elsewhere, to agree among themselves on a desirable total level of supplies and to administer themselves the necessary controls on imports to this country. Thus the Empire Beef Conference and an International Beef Conference, representing beef producers in the principal supplying countries, were formally entrusted by the British Government with the regulation of supplies to the United Kingdom of chilled and frozen beef from 1937. It was claimed that this process encouraged ' orderly marketing,' without prejudice to the meat consumption of the British housewives.

(2) *Subsidies*

The second type of assistance—subsidies on the output of specific products—certainly could not be criticised on the grounds of restricting supplies to consumers. The commodities principally concerned were sugar-beet, wheat, fat cattle, oats and barley. Grants to support the prices of milk products were given to the Milk Marketing Board ; a price insurance scheme for fat sheep was about to come into operation in the autumn of 1939 but was then suspended.

Of these subsidies, that for sugar-beet alone existed before the Great Depression. The First World War cut off the supplies of beet-sugar from the Continent which supplied an important part of Britain's imports, and the sugar shortage was one of the most urgent and most enduring of war-time scarcities. In 1925 a ten-year subsidy was granted to revive the growing of sugar-beet in this country ; the subsidy was to be progressively reduced during the decade in the hopes that, when well established, the industry would be able to compete unsubsidised with other countries. But during this period there were striking improvements in the technique of the tropical sugar-cane industry, which enabled larger supplies to be provided at substantially lower costs, while the general price fall from 1929 reduced both the cane and beet industries to temporary insolvency. The Greene Committee in 1934 could not agree whether the subsidy should be continued or not, since it was now probable that the home industry would never attain financial independence. The Government accepted the minority report and continued the subsidy on two grounds—firstly, the value of a local supply of sugar in time of war; and secondly, the financial plight of arable farmers who in the eastern areas derived from sugar-beet both a cash return and the advantages of a root break in their crop rotation.

The Wheat Act, 1932, provided a 'standard' price to farmers of 10s a cwt. for millable wheat sold to an approved buyer; the difference between this price and the average annual market price was paid to growers from a fund raised by a levy on every sack of flour. The levy was small in relation to the price of flour—it varied from 2d to 2s 7d per cwt.— because even when home production was at its highest it provided only one-fifth of the total wheat supplies required by the flour mills. The standard price was further linked to a maximum quantity of 27 million cwt. (raised in 1937 to 36 million cwt.) in such a way that sales in excess of this quantity brought a proportionate reduction in the deficiency payment.

The immediate effect of this measure was to encourage the production of wheat at the expense of other grain crops wherever conditions were reasonably favourable to wheat. There were many complaints that the principal subsidies provided for British agriculture favoured only those comparatively few districts that both grew wheat and were within reach of the sugar-beet factories situated with one exception on the eastern side of the country. By the Agriculture Act, 1937, a price insurance scheme linked to a standard oat price of 8s a cwt. was provided for both oats and barley. The payments, due if the market price of oats fell below this level, were to be paid in accordance with the acreage returned in the June census of each year; they could not be linked to the quantities sold (as occurred with wheat) since a substantial part of the oat crop was used for animal fodder without passing through a market. The subsidy on barley production was linked, rather illogically, to the price of oats for adminis-

trative convenience ; the market for barley was divided be-
between a highly specialised demand from the maltsters and
distillers and a general sale for feeding barley. But the
unusually good harvest of 1937 brought a heavy fall in prices
for all types of barley, and negotiations went on through 1938
and 1939 for an agreement, between the farmers on the one
hand and the maltsters and distillers on the other, for some
form of minimum prices for some guaranteed quantity of the
home crop.

In addition to these measures to maintain production of
the three grain crops, a subsidy was provided for fat cattle.
This was introduced as a temporary measure in 1934, when
it was hoped that the restrictions on meat imports would
effect in due course a rise in prices. But prices remained
obstinantly low, and the cattle subsidy was put on a permanent
basis by the Livestock Industry Act, 1937. A Livestock
Commission was established to administer the subsidy of
7s 6d a cwt. for first quality and of 5s a cwt. for second quality
fat beasts. The Commission was also instructed to prepare
schemes to improve the processes of marketing, but no progress
had been made before the outbreak of war. The payment
of the subsidy received but a tepid welcome from the
farmers, who complained that in some cases the butchers
and dealers combined at the auction sales to depress prices
by the amount of the subsidy, so that farmers obtained little
benefit.

It was not until a second collapse of prices in 1937–8,
associated with unusually heavy marketings, that assistance
was provided for sellers of fat sheep. A price insurance
scheme, linked to a standard price of 10d a lb. (dead weight),
was designed to come into operation in the autumn of 1939,
but as already stated it never took effect.

The total amount provided under these various schemes
varied of course with the market prices of the commodities
concerned ; the table below summarises the details for the
three pre-war years. The amounts must be correlated with
the value of the total agricultural output estimated at
£264½ millions in 1937–8 :

ESTIMATED AMOUNT OF SUBSIDIES AND GRANTS [1]
TO U.K. AGRICULTURE

	1935-6	1936-7	1937-8
	£'000's	£'000's	£'000's
Sugar[a] : Subsidy	2,620	2,580	1,240
Remission of Excise duty	2,440	2,680	1,970
Wheat[b]	5,640	1,340	1,930
Milk[c] : Manufacturing milk	900	210	40
Clean milk	10	50	130
Milk in schools	450	460	530
Other	40	50	40
Fat Cattle[c]	3,950	3,940	4,050
Barley and Oats[b]	—	—	170
Lime[d]	—	—	1,130
Basic Slag[d]	—	—	270
	16,050	11,310	11,500

[a] Sept.–Aug.   [b] to March 1938   [c] Oct.–Sept.   [d] year 1938

(3) Marketing Legislation

The marketing legislation of these years derived from three strands of thought. From the First World War, attempts were made to improve the quality, grading and packaging of the home produce sold in competition with imported supplies which were usually inspected, graded and bulked at the port of shipment in appropriate units for the British market. The National Mark Scheme, introduced in 1927, had a limited success for minor products such as eggs and apples, but little was done for other and more important products.

A second criticism of marketing in these years arose from the increasing complexities of the processing trades, which put farmers further in the powers of the wholesalers. There were many complaints, some justified and some unfounded, that farmers bought and sold in markets where the prices they paid or received unduly favoured the numerically fewer wholesalers.

[1] *Agricultural Register 1938–9*, p. 50 (Agricultural Economics Research Institute, Oxford 1939)

Co-operative buying and selling was often recommended as a method both of reducing the costs of intermediary processes and of strengthening the bargaining power of the farmers. Co-operative buying of farm requisites was well established before the First World War in certain districts, but co-operative selling was less successful for a variety of reasons. Dairy farmers in the south of England benefited from the annual settlement of wholesale milk prices between the National Farmers' Union and representatives of the wholesale dairymen ; Scottish farmers experimented unsuccessfully with a selling agency in Glasgow and more successfully in Aberdeen. Hop growers, comparatively few in numbers, followed up the war-time Hop Control with a co-operative society to negotiate the annual price of hops with the brewers, but increasing stocks and rising production from the unco-operative minority brought its liquidation after the 1929 crop. These experiences led farmers to argue that voluntary co-operation could do little to counteract monopolistic tendencies in the wholesale trades without some form of compulsion upon all sellers of the product concerned.

Finally, the collapse of prices after 1929 brought urgent appeals to the Government from the farming interest. The fall in prices was so severe and so general that no conceivable reduction in costs or change in type of production could restore a margin of profit in time to save thousands of farmers from bankruptcy. The limited degree of organisation in the retail milk market broke down completely after 1930, while production continued to increase beyond the declining capacity of the British housewives to buy. More than 20 per cent of the industrial workers were unemployed in 1932, but while demand declined, imports and home production continued to increase. Restriction of supplies became the accepted remedy for the falling prices, a restriction which in this country was to be applied firstly to the rising tide of imports and only as a last resort to the British farmer.

The Agricultural Marketing Acts, 1931 and 1933, enabled the producers of any agricultural product to set up a marketing board, elected by them, which should negotiate the conditions and terms of sale, control the grade, description or type of product to be sold, and if necessary enforce a restriction of output upon its members. After the due processes of law had been fulfilled, the Boards could enforce these conditions upon all sellers of the prescribed product by the imposition of financial penalties for infringements of its bye-laws. The Boards could themselves buy, sell, store or process the prescribed product or its derivatives, and it was hoped that these powers would be used to improve and cheapen the various stages of marketing that stretch between farmers and consumers.

Marketing Boards were established under these Acts for two crops—potatoes and hops ; and for two livestock products —milk and bacon pigs. Those for pigs had a chequered career, and the system of sales on annual contracts to the bacon curers was in abeyance at the outbreak of war. Since we are here concerned with these Boards for the purpose of war-time action and of post-war developments, the reader is referred to other sources for an account of their organisation and operations.[1]

After five years of experience, opinion just before the war tended to be unfavourable to any further extension of producer marketing boards ; it is noteworthy that no new Board was established after 1934, in spite of proposals to organise in this fashion the producers of eggs, table poultry and raspberries (in Scotland). After this date other forms of assistance were provided for sellers of fat cattle and sheep and for growers of oats and barley. That the operations of the Boards for hops, potatoes and milk conferred considerable benefits on their registered producers was generally agreed, but there was a growing volume of criticism against the maintenance of retail prices by the Milk Marketing Board. Forming producers into a monopoly was supposed to counteract any monopolistic tendencies among wholesalers, but two monopolies were found not to cancel out but to add up. The Milk

[1] See, in particular, *Report of the Lucas Committee on the Working of the Agricultural Marketing Acts* (H.M.S.O. 1949) ; Thomas, *An Introduction to Agricultural Economics*, chapter xii (Nelson, 1949)

Marketing Board, concerned to obtain higher and more secure prices for milk sold retail in the liquid market, included in its contracts a clause requiring the maintenance of minimum wholesale and retail margins, thus safeguarding the remuneration of its own wholesale customers. The Consumers' Committee established under the Agriculture Marketing Acts complained frequently and vehemently against the lack of competition and rising prices in this retail market ; on the other hand, the general public benefited from the Board's efforts to improve the quality of the milk supplied and from the provision of cheap milk to school children. A Government subsidy to maintain minimum prices for milk sold for manufacture was also criticised ; any subsidy, it was argued, should be devoted to reducing prices and increasing sales in the liquid market, which would then absorb a higher proportion of the total supplies of milk.

The Hops Marketing Board attracted less general interest since it was necessarily on a smaller scale than the Milk Marketing Board for England and Wales. But criticism was not wanting of the undesirable example set by this Board in establishing a legal monopoly in the production of hops. No-one could sell hops who had not been a grower in the years just before the scheme came into force, and established growers could not exceed the acreage grown in that period. By these means and by the periodic destruction of hops which were not bought at the agreed price of £9 per cwt., the Hops Marketing Board succeeded in restoring a profitable level of returns to the original growers, a degree of profitability which was quickly reflected in the enhanced prices paid for farms which had a ' quota for hops.' The claim for stable markets and reasonable prices which aroused much sympathy in 1929–33 should not, it was felt, justify the legal authorisation of a monopoly formed by those who happened to be sellers of a commodity at one particular date.

By 1939 there was therefore a certain disillusionment over the results of the Agricultural Marketing Acts ; it was felt that too little attention had been paid to the interests of consumers in better and cheaper marketing and too much emphasis placed on price maintenance and restriction of supplies. But indirectly the existence of these marketing boards and of the Wheat and Livestock Commissions greatly eased the transition from peace to war in September 1939. They had collected a mass of information concerning the production and processing of their products ; they had trained and informed administrators, many of whom assisted the Food (Defence Plans) Department in the last year of peace and later joined the Ministry of Food. The regulation of saleable supplies by the Potato Marketing Board, the registration of contracts and the monthly notification of producer sales obtained by the Milk Marketing Boards, the grading of cattle by the Livestock Commission, the register of approved buyers kept by the Wheat Commission, these functions and the officials who performed them were easily adapted to the more comprehensive controls required in war.

BIBLIOGRAPHY

For the First World War and the inter-war years in general :

MIDDLETON, SIR THOMAS, *Food Production in War* (O.U.P. 1923)

LAYTON, SIR WALTER, and CROWTHER, G., *Introduction to the Study of Prices*, 3rd edition (Macmillan 1938)

VENN, J. A., *Foundations of Agricultural Economics*, chapter xxii onwards, 2nd edition (Cambridge 1933)

ASTOR, LORD, and ROWNTREE, S., *British Agriculture* (Longmans 1938)

ORR, J. B., *Food, Health and Income* (Macmillan 1938)

National Farm Survey, England and Wales (H.M.S.O. 1946)

Ministry of Agriculture Economic Series (H.M.S.O.)

CHAPTER II

FOOD DEFENCE PLANS

THE experience of 1914 to 1919 produced two principles for feeding the nation during a long war—the need to grow more food at home to mitigate the loss of imports, and the need to control the food available.

Shipping Shortage and its Effects

A shortage of shipping was the natural result of the activity of enemy submarines round British ports and especially in the Atlantic, across which came the greatest volume of supplies ; in addition, war created an intensified demand for shipping not only to bring munitions into this country but to carry men and materials to distant battlefields. A scarcity of ships, whether caused by loss at sea or by increased demand for military purposes, could best be countered by economies in bulky cargoes of grain and oil-seeds, and by the conversion of British agriculture to produce the greatest volume of food, to produce cereals, potatoes and vegetables for human consumption instead of grass and fodder crops for animals. Such a policy meant in 1917 a radical diversion of the accustomed diet towards bulky vegetarian foods which could be grown at home ; the shipping space saved could be used to import supplementary foods of high food value and relatively small bulk, such as fats, meat, sugar and bacon. The loss of imported feedingstuffs and the transference of cereals from animals to humans meant a brief glut of meat while a drastic reduction took place in the livestock population. Pigs and poultry were most affected since they were most dependent on cereals, and there was also a drastic decline in the flocks of lowland sheep, whose pastures were ploughed for wheat and potatoes. In the latter stages of the war, the output of milk was also reduced since the dairy cows suffered from lack of cereals and oilcake. These were the inevitable results of a sudden shortage of cereals.

Price Control and Food Rationing

The second main principle was the need both for price control and for food rationing, so that the unavoidable scarcities should be distributed as equitably as possible between rich and poor, and between the urban and rural housewives. Fair shares for all implied control of the major foods imported into or produced within the country, so that they could be redistributed through wholesalers and retailers to supply the consumers' rations. The price system and the profit motive were recognised as inapplicable to the task of rationing war-time scarcities, however efficient they might be judged to be in times of peace in adjusting production to consumer preferences. No preferences could be allowed in war-time, other than those dictated by military necessity.

The experience of the First World War gave no clue, however, to an appropriate price policy for agriculture. Prices had then been uncontrolled until they had risen from twice to three times the 1914 level, and from 1917 onwards the efforts of the Government had been directed to preventing any further increase. It was generally agreed that in any future war the prices of the major foods should be controlled from the outset ; voluntary agreements, not to exceed current prices in the first few weeks of war, were obtained from the wholesale and retail trades and the marketing boards in order to give time for maximum prices to be prescribed under the Defence Regulations. Control by the Government of the most important prices paid to farmers implied future decisions on price policy. Should prices be kept to the pre-war level in order to keep down the cost of living to the consumer ? Would farmers' prices and their profits have to be increased in order to obtain the desired increase in food production, and if so, by how much and for what products ? If we needed more grain and fewer sheep, should grain prices be raised and sheep prices lowered ? What was likely to happen to farmers' costs, in particular to the costs of imported feedingstuffs and of labour ? Agricultural wages were considerably below the level of earnings in most other industries, and this inferiority was certainly one great cause of that ' drift from the land ' which would surely need to be checked, if not reversed, before a food-production campaign could be effective. For many grassland farmers, too, ploughing for victory would mean the purchase of implements which might only be required for a few seasons—a heavy addition to their usual costs. On these matters, no announcement had been made before the Second World War, and subsequent events showed that they had indeed received little attention.

These two basic principles, valuable though they were, were thus not in themselves a sufficient guide to the food defence plans for a Second World War. We should inevitably need a ploughing campaign to grow more cereals ; we should need a Ministry of Food to organise the distribution of food from the farms and ports to the shops and to control prices. But what degree of shipping shortage could we expect in another war in which air attack might be as dangerous as the submarine attacks of 1917 ? For on the shortage of imports depended the intensity of the food-production campaign designed to fill the gap and the price policy to go with it.

Just before the Second World War, the United Kingdom annually imported 8–9 million tons of animal feedingstuffs, and 4 million tons of bread grains primarily for human consumption. A mild degree of shipping shortage would lead logically to a cut in the imports of feedingstuffs and to an increased production of them at home in order to maintain the output of meat and milk, but a severe reduction in imports which imperilled the basic rations of the population implied a reversion to the conditions of 1917—a planned reduction in the numbers of livestock, the conversion of cereals into human foodstuffs and a diet that was substantially vegetarian. In these circumstances, the advance of nutritional science made one change from the earlier theory ; the importance of milk was now emphasised as a source of vitamins as well as an essential ingredient in the diet of expectant mothers, babies and young children. It was also known that the dairy cow was the most economical converter of animal fodder into human food. In a condition of extreme shipping shortage, therefore, British agriculture would be required to provide not only the largest possible quantity of the basic cereals and of vegetables but sufficient feedingstuffs to supply a certain minimum of milk.

Other complications could also be foreseen. It was possible, indeed probable, that our ability to import might be more rapidly restricted by lack of foreign exchange to buy in neutral countries than by submarine attacks. In that event it might be better to import the cheap bulky cereals, if ships were available, and to produce at home more of the expensive meats and dairy produce. A combination of some degree of shipping shortage and some degree of scarcity of foreign exchange was the most probable development, but which was likely to be dominant in the early stages of a great war ? Should agriculture be asked to produce more cereals in order to support more animals or in order to feed human beings directly at the expense of the animals ?

Ploughing Campaign and Food Storage

These eventualities could not easily be weighed before the outbreak of war, but in any case a ploughing campaign—the conversion of grassland to crops—was a necessary start. In the three or four years before the war there was much argument over the best and cheapest method of securing a higher acreage of arable in the early years of any war. For time was the essence of food production plans. If war was declared in the winter or spring, eighteen months would elapse before the results of a ploughing campaign would be available whether to feed animals or humans ; it would take, it was reckoned, at least two such ploughings to bring agricultural production to its peak. Was it advisable as a precautionary measure to maintain the arable acreage at more than its peace-time level ? What would be the effect on the number of cargo ships available to Britain in war-time of a permanent reduction in the demand for bulky cargoes in times of peace ? Would a policy of food storage not be a cheaper and less damaging method of tiding over the first year or so of war ?

The balance of arguments between food storage and intensified food production was fairly even, and a mixture of both was finally adopted by the Government. In the last eighteen months before the war, stores were acquired of three basic foods—wheat, sugar and whale oil, one of the basic constituents of margarine. Meanwhile the Agriculture Act 1937 had provided two measures designed primarily as precaution against war. The amount of wheat eligible for the standard price of 10s per cwt. was raised from 27 to 36 million cwt., and an acreage grant, linked to a minimum price, was provided for oats and barley. These two measures, it was hoped, gave an inducement to maintain the total area under grain. In addition, a subsidy was provided to cheapen the cost to farmers of lime and basic slag applied to grassland ; the experience of the First World War had showed that a large part of British grassland was deficient in lime and phosphates to such an extent that crop failures might be frequently expected after ploughing.

In the last year of peace, after the dismemberment of Czechoslovakia, further preparations were developed. There was the problem of getting the first year's ploughing executed in perhaps a few weeks. In 1917 the amount ploughed had necessarily been limited by the working powers of the existing population of horses ; in 1939 the tractors already on the farms provided a welcome addition, but they were highly concentrated in the existing arable districts. More mechanical power would urgently be required in the grassland counties, and the Ministry of Agriculture provided reserves of tractors and implements for release after the outbreak of war. And finally, in April 1939, a grant of £2 per acre was offered for grassland ploughed in 1939–40 and reseeded or sown to an approved crop, while financial assistance was to be provided on a wider scale for land drainage. Both these measures were valuable preliminaries to war-time action, and would at the same time increase the output and improve the efficiency of many acres of grassland.

Agricultural Executive Committees

Whatever might be the production policy to be adopted in the event of war, the Agricultural Departments would require local agents who could adapt the broad principles of a national programme to the peculiarities of local conditions and customs. ' Farming from Whitehall ' was a slogan calculated to arouse the contempt of any practical farmer, but some unfortunate individuals had to form the chain between the plans of the Government and the plans of farmers for their individual fields and flocks. During 1938 and 1939 more than 600 men and women were nominated to form Agricultural Executive Committees in each county in England and Wales or in each ' district ' in Scotland. The Ministry of Agriculture drew heavily on the agricultural staff of the county councils to fill the important posts of executive officers to these committees, thus obtaining men who had local knowledge and who were already known to the farmers in their area.

So much had been achieved when Hitler's armies invaded Poland on 1 September 1939. The Agricultural Executive Committees sprang into being, armed with extensive powers to direct, control and persuade in furtherance of food production. The Food (Defence Plans) Department, which had been formed in 1936, was converted within a week into a Ministry of Food, absorbing the staff and functions of most of the agricultural marketing boards and many members of the wholesale and retail food trades. The end of the twenty years and ten months of uneasy peace found in excellent starting order that administrative machinery for a ploughing campaign which was so completely absent in August 1914.

CHAPTER III

FIRST YEAR OF WAR, 1939-40

THOSE who directed the food production campaign had a clear conception of the first task to be tackled—the ploughing of grassland, but beyond that immediate action, agricultural policy in the first few months of war was confused. There seem to have been misunderstandings first on the nature of the war into which we had plunged, and secondly on the speed at which it was desirable to introduce the planned measures for price control and food rationing.

Shipping and Production Policy

Would there or would there not be a scarcity of ships to bring bulky cargoes ? The Government was quick to announce that no interruption was to be expected to the normal supply of wheat and of feedingstuffs. At the same time there was a call to farmers to plough 2 million acres, 10 per cent of the existing area of permanent grass ; they were to plant it with wheat or potatoes, or if these crops were unlikely to give a reasonable yield, with feedingstuffs for animals.

This appeal, with its similarity to that of 1917, met with a satisfactory response as far as the ploughing was concerned. By June 1940, indeed, it was found that slightly more than 2 million acres had been added to the arable area of the United Kingdom. But the recommendation on crops aroused some little comment. Why grow more wheat if there was to be no scarcity of it ? The absence of such scarcity was generally deduced from the absence of any legal prohibition against the feeding of the 1939 harvest to animals ; if the Government expected any scarcity to develop, they would surely secure the current crop for human consumption, it was argued. Nor were farmers at first enthusiastic over the appeal for more potatoes. If there was to be no food scarcity of any sort, would people buy more potatoes if grown ?

And if they did not, who would pay for the unsold stocks? The Potato Marketing Board (together with the three Boards concerned with pigs) had been put into cold storage at the outbreak of war and its functions suspended, so that no mechanism existed to provide a guaranteed market for a harvest in excess of normal. That deficiency was, however, realised before the planting season; in December the Agricultural Departments announced that the existing levy on all potatoes sold by wholesalers would be used to pay the market price for potatoes that could not be sold in the usual way.

Another confusion arose in the second month of war, when the Minister of Agriculture announced that fat sheep prices (then controlled at the pre-war level) would shortly be raised by 2d per lb. in order to encourage farmers to breed more sheep. It was desirable, he said, to forestall a possible scarcity of imported meat in the future by producing more at home. Since no substantial increase in numbers of fat cattle could be expected within the next two or three years, the best means of achieving this end quickly was an expansion in the sheep population, bearing in mind that sheep need not consume any appreciable quantity of imported feedingstuffs.

This announcement overlooked the fact that a large proportion of the sheep population spent much of their short lives in lowland pastures. Ought farmers to keep more sheep and grow more fodder for them or to plough their grazing for wheat and potatoes? The problem was not simplified when, at the end of November, farmers first experienced that shortage of imported feedingstuffs which had been impending, apparently unnoticed, since the outbreak of war. The suspension of normal trade in the last few weeks of peace, the delays necessitated by the introduction of convoys and by other measures of defence all combined to reduce substantially the arrivals of grain. A situation had quickly developed which resembled (though with less intensity) that of 1917. There was too little grain to feed both the human population and the animal population at pre-war standards; the remedy, increased home production, could not be effective for another nine months. Meanwhile there was a severe cut, amounting to one-third or more of peace-time consumption, in imported cereals, a cut which affected most severely specialist pig and poultry holdings and densely stocked dairy farms which could grow little for themselves.   Even on ordinary farms the breeding of more sheep was out of the question when farmers needed the pastures to grow rape, oats, kale and beans for their existing flocks, their cows and beef cattle.

The early emphasis on the production of more wheat and potatoes was changed early in December, when the shortage of feedingstuffs was painfully apparent.   Farmers were then urged to plan mainly for an increased production of feeding-stuffs in the harvest of 1940, though the Government would allow them, the Minister explained, complete freedom to crop as they wished.   Though there would be a substantial cut in the volume of imported feeding cereals, the Minister hoped that wheat supplies could be maintained from imports, and that farmers would maintain the output of meat and milk, using a higher proportion of home-grown feeds.

The cropping policy for the 1940 harvest was thus left largely to the good sense of the farmers, who did in the event provide substantially more oats, barley and potatoes.   The ploughing of more than 2 million acres of grassland in addition to the normal area shows the enthusiasm with which they went to work, aided by the tractor service organised through each county Agricultural Executive Committee in England and Wales [1] and by the Department of Agriculture throughout Scotland.   The shortage of feedingstuffs no doubt provided a strong inducement to grow more as a precautionary measure against the scarcities that might be expected in the winter of 1940–1.

There were indeed many prophecies during the winter of 1939–40 that numbers of livestock would be drastically reduced before the spring because of lack of feedingstuffs. Sad stories were told of the premature deaths inflicted on growing pigs and laying hens in order to prevent them dying

[1] South of the Border, they were officially styled War Agricultural Executive Committees, and were thus usually known among farmers as 'the War Ag.'

of starvation.   When the June returns became available in the
summer of 1940, they showed a rather different picture.
There was indeed a slight decline compared with 1939 in
the number of breeding sows, and a marked fall in the number
of sheep being kept for breeding in the year 1940-1.   But
the feature of these statistics was the increase over the first
year of war in the number of animals of all species kept for
fattening—cattle over two years old, pigs over five months
old, sheep over one year.   A shortage of feedingstuffs slowed
up the rate of growth for these animals and caused a marked
deficit in the numbers sent for slaughter in the first six months
of 1940.   Cattle and sheep that would normally have been
slaughtered from January onwards were being fattened off
the summer grass in June and would arrive on the market
in the autumn when sales were always at a maximum.   If
farmers were intending as well to reduce their breeding stocks
of sheep and beef cattle, the doomed animals were also
peacefully grazing the summer grass.   An unusually large
supply of fat stock was clearly impending for the autumn
months.   And from the early days of September 1940, the
offerings at the collecting centres exceeded the capacity of the
slaughter-houses to kill and the capacity of consumers to buy
and eat.   For some weeks the Ministry of Food was unable
to accept all the sheep and cattle entered for slaughter in
spite of a substantial increase in the ration and the suspension
of sales of imported meat.   The temporary glut of home-killed
meat experienced in 1917 was thus repeated in 1940.

COSTS AND PRICES

At the outbreak of war the new Ministry of Food had
successfully stabilised many food prices at the levels prevailing
in July and August.   Because of the pressure of work in
those hectic days, the maximum prices applied only to the
major commodities with the minimum number of grades
and qualities.   A maximum buying price had thus been fixed
for wheat at 7s per cwt., leaving the 'standard' price unchanged
at 10s, but there had not been time to deal with other grains.

Maximum prices at current levels had also been prescribed for all fat stock—cattle, fat cows, sheep and pigs ; these were to be shortly followed by more detailed schedules to come into operation with the rationing of meat, six or eight weeks after the outbreak of war.

But the introduction of food rationing was repeatedly postponed, partly because of the unexpected complexity of the necessary preparations and partly because its desirability, as a weapon of war, was not unquestioned. Because Britain was compelled by sudden scarcity to ration food in 1917, was it really necessary to repeat the performance in 1939 when supplies were ample ? The argument might have continued long, but the level of imports fell so sharply in the first few weeks of the war as to endanger the stocks (and eventually the consumption level) first of wheat, then of iron-ore and finally of feedingstuffs, which were deliberately sacrificed to the rebuilding of wheat stocks. The rationing of meat and bacon early in 1940 was followed later by that of sugar, tea, butter and margarine ; the Ministry of Food became the sole buyer, through its authorised agents, of all rationed foods.

The delay of five months between the preliminary schedule of maximum prices for fat stock and the start of the full control scheme was an uncomfortable hiatus. By November there were many complaints over the existing maximum prices, which perpetuated into a season of rising prices a level which was regarded as unusually low ; and further, all through these weeks farmers' costs were rising. The prices of imported products—petrol and oil, fertilisers, feedingstuffs— were rapidly increased by the depreciation of sterling, by rising freight rates and by the need for insurance against war risks ; and from November onwards the scarcity of imported cereals led to a sharp rise in the prices for home-grown oats and barley. Falling total supplies and an unchanged demand for them had the normal result ; prices rose ; farmers with supplies to sell held them off the market in the hope of a further rise, and by the end of January the prices of these ' less essential ' cereals were more than double their pre-war level and were still rising, with obvious effects on the costs of producing milk, fat cattle and other livestock.

This unexpected development, which might, one feels, have been foreseen the moment it was known that cereal imports were below normal, had some inconvenient results. Wheat prices had been controlled at the outbreak of war at current levels, but a month later the 'standard' prices for wheat and oats of the 1939 harvest were both raised by 1s per cwt. (to 11s and 8s a cwt. respectively) as an inducement to greater production in 1940. Such a measure paled into insignificance beside the later rise in market prices ; even when oat prices were controlled from 1 February (at 11s per cwt. for feeding oats, at 12s per cwt. for milling oats), the relationship thus established with the price of wheat was the inverse of that normally found.

Secondly, this rise in prices for home-grown oats implied a similar price for the imported product (since the two were often indistinguishable from each other), and there was therefore yet one more rise in costs for those farmers who bought oats for feeding livestock. By November these farmers were claiming substantially increased prices for fat stock to cover their increased costs and to include the usual seasonal trend of upward prices for the Christmas trade. To maintain the existing prices over this period was clearly impossible ; indeed the controlled prices were admittedly ineffective in some markets, but it was found to be administratively impracticable to negotiate and enforce a temporary schedule for this brief period before meat rationing and the full control scheme came into force. For several weeks therefore there was no price control over fat stock ; the new schedule of fixed prices introduced in January provided for an increase of one-quarter (compared with average prices in January 1939) in fat-cattle prices and of nearly one-third for pigs.

The settlement of these new prices provided weighty problems for administrators. There was, in the first place, the reaction of these higher prices to producers on the retail prices of meat and bacon paid by the consumer, a matter discussed in the next chapter. Secondly, there were grave difficulties in calculating just how much costs had risen because of dearer feedingstuffs. Thirdly, it was by no means clear whether, when a rise in costs had been established, prices ought to be adjusted to allow for the calculated rise in costs, for the calculated rise in costs plus something more, or for less than the calculated rise in costs. These two last points must be discussed in turn.

A rise in costs such as that which occurred in the autumn of 1939 did not affect all livestock producers equally. Some farmers were entirely dependent on purchased feeds, growing little or nothing for their own stock ; there were thousands of small holdings keeping pigs and poultry on this basis, and many dairy farmers, especially in Lancashire and Yorkshire, also provided little except grazing for their cows. But other farmers kept a few pigs or poultry to consume tail corn or chat potatoes or whey from cheese making ; they combined crop production with a dairy herd which fed on sugar-beet tops, kale or silage as well as a ration of dairy nuts from the corn merchant. A rise in the price of purchased grain affected these two groups of farmers quite differently, yet it was administratively impossible to distinguish between them when it came to price adjustments. From cost accounts already collected from certain representative types of farm, it was possible to calculate roughly how much the total costs of producing milk or pigs or beef cattle had been affected on these farms by the changes in feedingstuff prices ; something might be added on to allow for farms whose costs might have been increased more than the representative group ; the result could only be a rough approximation to the changes in costs which might have been experienced on thousands of farms if they had maintained unaltered pre-war practices.

But, of course, a sudden rise in the prices of feedingstuffs induced a long series of changes in habits and practices as farmers tried other combinations in order to keep down their costs. Here again the scope for economies in the use of purchased feeds varied greatly ; again it was the small specialised holding which could do least in the way of adaptation and the ordinary mixed farm which could achieve most.

By more careful feeding of individual animals, by more economical use of home-grown feeds, such as hay or silage, many farmers found that the rise in their costs was substantially less than had at first been expected. Yet it was administratively impossible to allow for these varying factors, and indeed it was not likely that they would receive much attention ; the Milk Marketing Board and the National Farmers' Unions who conducted the negotiations on these matters were naturally more concerned with those farmers whose costs had been affected more than the average, and who had for various reasons little scope for adaptations. In these circumstances there was inevitably a tendency to estimate the new level of costs with a generous margin ; to aim not at an average cost but at one which included the large majority of farms while it might yet underestimate the change which had occurred on a minority of holdings.

The calculation of a change in costs was therefore both complex and imprecise ; and its achievement by no means solved the problem of what price to fix. To suggest that if costs, however calculated, had risen by 10 per cent since August 1939, milk prices or pig prices should automatically be increased by the same proportion ignored the important influence of prices in securing from farmers the type of production required.

One way of obtaining from a total of more than 300,000 farmers a greater output of certain commodities is to raise prices relatively to costs and thus to increase the profit margin for these particular products. Given time and an expectation that these differential profits will continue for a reasonable period, some farmers already producing these commodities will produce more, either through higher yields from existing acres or animals, or by growing less of some competing and less profitable product. Other farmers, making unsatisfactory returns from their existing enterprises, will turn some of their productive resources to the more profitable uses. Not all farmers of course will be able to effect such a transference ; technical factors such as soil or climate may hinder them, or they may be unable to raise the capital required to buy new equipment, or they may have neither the knowledge nor the willingness to produce, say, milk instead of beef. Yet in spite of the farms that are for various reasons unable to adapt, a shift in profit margins between commodities has in the past evoked a corresponding response in production as farmers attempt to secure the best possible results from the resources at their disposal.

The application of this theory to the circumstances of 1939 was fairly simple for those products of which a greater output was required. Having calculated the probable rise in costs per unit of output by the mixture of statistics and guesswork described above, it was necessary to increase the pre-war price by the same percentage in order to maintain unchanged the pre-war rate of profit, and therefore presumably to maintain unchanged the pre-war level of output. But since a greater output was required, an increase in price proportionately greater than the change in unit costs was indicated in order to induce farmers to devote extra resources to these commodities, and to provide necessary capital. Unfortunately no evidence was available to show by how much, in the circumstances of 1939, prices of these commodities should be raised in order to achieve, say, a 10 per cent increase in output ; the changes made merely reflected official opinion about the psychological effects, on farmers' willingness to produce, of an increase in certain prices seen in relation to the probable level of costs in the future.

This approach had been used soon after the outbreak of war, when the standard prices of wheat and oats had been raised ; and when sheep prices were raised in an abortive attempt to increase the output of fat sheep. But pig prices could not be so easily dealt with. When the shortage of feedingstuffs developed in November, the Government had warned producers that they could not count on more than two-thirds of the pre-war supplies and recommended a corresponding reduction in the numbers of pigs and poultry. A fall in prices is the normal indication that output should be cut, but such a course of action was strongly contested. Confronted with the certainty of a smaller turnover, representatives of the specialist producers of pigs and poultry urged that the margin between costs and prices should be increased, as output fell, so as to give an unchanged income. Many of these holdings were entirely dependent on purchased feeds ; they were often quite unsuited to other types of production since they consisted merely of an acre or less of rough grazings, with fattening pens or chicken runs as their only equipment. Higher cereal prices meant for them higher food costs without giving an opportunity to produce their own grain.

The best method of securing a fall in output of selected commodities was indeed one of the great problems of the early years of war. To allow an uncompensated rise in costs to reduce the profit margin from their production meant the rapid extinction of these small specialised units. To allow, for their sake, an increase in profit margins as their intake of feeds and their output fell gave an unwanted inducement to the general farmer to feed to pigs or poultry the grain that might be more urgently required to maintain the output of milk or the supply of breadstuffs. In this first year there seems to have been a tendency, exemplified by the increase in pig prices, to grant a substantial part of the claims of the specialised units for higher margins as output fell ; it was not until another eighteen months had passed that the problem solved itself when the exclusion of all imported feedingstuffs virtually extinguished the specialist pig holdings. Changes in the pre-war costs of producing pigs from a carefully balanced ration of milling offals, barley and fishmeal had no relevance to the war-time pig fed mainly on swill and waste potatoes.

By the spring of 1940 there was therefore in the agricultural price structure a considerable element of irrationality in the sense that much of it was unintended and uncorrelated with production policy. The need for some rise in profits had been recognised as an inducement to an expanded output of cereals, and that implied that prices should be increased faster than costs. But the partial control of prices established early in the war had not led to a logical movement. Higher prices for oats and barley had resulted from the pressure of an unrationed demand on a rapidly falling supply ; there had been a deliberate, but much smaller, increase in wheat prices ; the price of sheep, it will be remembered, had been raised in order to induce an expansion in numbers which was impracticable. The main result of imperfect price control was thus to place at a relative disadvantage the production of three major commodities—wheat, milk and potatoes [1]—whose prices had been raised less than those of less important commodities—pigs, eggs, or malting barley. Much of the trouble experienced in later years can be traced to this unco-ordinated price structure established in the first winter of war, and revealed in the following statistics :

INDEX OF AGRICULTURAL PRICES [2]

	Average 1936–8	1939				1940	
		Mar.	June	Sept.	Dec.	Mar.	June
Wheat	100	99	99	113	113	113	113
Barley [a]	100	74	70	104	157	167	163
Oats [a]	100	82	83	83	157	172	150
Potatoes	100	75	55	77½	76½	90	99
Fat Cattle	100	103	108	112	122	133	140
Fat Sheep	100	106	95	92	104	129	116½
Bacon Pigs	100	107	97½	103½	143	148	151
Milk	100	117	85½	101	133	137½	103
Eggs	100	67	84	127	147½	114½	123
Total [b]	100	103½	91	104½	128	133	124

[a] Excluding subsidy payments ; [b] including other commodities

[1] The disadvantage for potatoes was less than appeared from a comparison of prices alone ; a guaranteed market for all sound potatoes appreciably raised total receipts from this crop, since a good yield usually left a substantial proportion unsold.

[2] Including exchequer payments on wheat and fat cattle ; not corrected for seasonal variation.

CHAPTER IV

THE MOBILISATION OF FARMING, 1940

THE first winter of war, that of 1939–40, was exceptionally severe. Snow in January and frost in February kept horse and tractor alike from the plough, and it was not until mid-March that the grey of winter pastures was succeeded by the browns, reds and yellows of newly turned furrows. The first of a long series of spring droughts speeded up the work ; the tractors operated in England and Wales by the Agricultural Executive Committees and in Scotland by the Department of Agriculture were fully employed all through the spring for farmers inadequately supplied with cultivating equipment. More than two million acres of grassland were ploughed in the United Kingdom, thus exceeding the target announced at the outbreak of war. The Government's early call for wheat had met with little response, due partly to the wet October, but farmers, remembering the hungry days of 1917, had planted 130,000 acres more with potatoes, and there was a substantial increase in the acreage under oats and barley. All types of grain flourished in the hot dry summer ; though the hay crop was light, yields of other crops were generally above average and exceptionally so for potatoes. That high yield was fortunate ; combined with the greater area, it enabled a still larger acreage to be planted in 1941 without restricting the supply of potatoes for human consumption in the winter of 1940–1. The annual returns of crops and live-stock taken in June also showed that farmers had, perhaps wisely, ignored the official command of the previous autumn to increase the numbers of sheep ; far from an increase in breeding stock there was a small decline between 1939 and 1940, to be followed in the autumn of 1940 by a drastic reduction in flocks of lowland and arable sheep.

WAGES AND WORKERS

Some years before the war there had been discussions over the supply of manpower for a war-time agriculture. Two points were clear—the ploughing campaign would inevitably and eventually increase the need for farm workers, whose numbers had been steadily falling since the last quarter of the nineteenth century ; there would certainly be some recruitment for the armed services from the ranks of farm workers so that the outbreak of war might immediately intensify that shrinkage.

The various ministries concerned had worked out in the last pre-war months a system of controlled recruitment from agriculture. Men over 21 years of age engaged full time in agricultural work were not to be called up, though of course all existing members of the Territorial Army and other reserves were withdrawn at the outbreak of war irrespective of age. Those liable for military service between 18 and 21 could be reserved if they were ' key ' men for whom no satisfactory replacement could be found ; the advice of the appropriate Agricultural Executive Committees was sought on these matters before the formal decision was taken by the Ministry of Labour. After a year of war the general reservation of all men over 21 years was gradually abandoned ; and the process of individual reservation was applied to all farm workers at all the ages included in the general liability for service with the armed forces. The reservation, it should be noted, was granted because the man in question was judged to be indispensable and no satisfactory substitute could be found ; if a man so reserved changed his job he automatically lost his reservation.

Coupled with this restricted withdrawal of men for military service, the Women's Land Army was designed to supply partly trained substitutes who could carry on the work of food production. In spite of its military name, the W.L.A. was essentially a civilian force recruited by Government departments to be employed in a civilian industry. Because the conditions for women working in agriculture were largely unregulated and often unsatisfactory, certain minimum requirements in pay and housing were enforced on all employers of these volunteers, and the county committees of the W.L.A. kept a watchful eye on their work and welfare.

In the first winter of war the organisers of the W.L.A. were disturbed to find that demand from farmers was inadequate to absorb several thousand eager recruits. Farmers coped with the first ploughing campaign with substantially the same number of workers as they had in 1939; they drew on local unemployed or casually employed men to fill the loss of trained workers in the military reserves rather than on the unknown and largely inexperienced women of the Land Army.

But by the spring of 1940 wages in industrial occupations had steadily risen under the double impact of a rapid expansion in employment in engineering and munition-making and a rise in the cost of living. More immediate in its effect upon agriculture was the sudden burst of constructional work in rural districts; camps for the army and airfields for the Royal Air Force drew men from the farms in the neighbourhood for work which gave substantially higher earnings and, usually, shorter hours. Farmers, and Agricultural Executive Committees charged with the oversight of the ploughing campaign, protested against the drift of men from farms to seek better paid work; the agricultural trade unions maintained that only higher wages would retain men, and discounted the farmers' claims of their inability to pay more than the existing rate.

Minimum wage rates for farm workers were indeed rising in the first months of war; but the increase was geographically uneven, and was in any case less than the increase in most industrial occupations, so that the disparity between urban and rural earnings was also growing. There was strong pressure for a national minimum wage which would even up the existing differences in the local minima established by the county Wage Committees, and in spite of some opposition from the farmers the constitution of the central Wages Board in England and Wales was altered early in 1940 to enable it to fix a national minimum wage for farm workers.

While the Board was slowly digesting its new powers other events occurred—the German attack on Norway which brought into office the Coalition Government headed by Mr Churchill, the invasion of Belgium, Holland and France, and the occupation of the coastline of north-east Europe by the enemy. In this setting, the three-fold problem of food production, the supply of workers required for it and the prices to be paid acquired a new urgency and a new atmosphere. The new Government agreed that the agricultural output must be intensified as rapidly as possible ; that agricultural wages should be raised to equality with industrial earnings so that existing farm workers could be compelled to remain in agriculture ; that prices to be paid to farmers for their products must be raised to enable them to pay these wages and to grow the food required.

Prompted by the Government the two central Wages Boards declared a national minimum wage for the adult male farm worker of 48s a week, an increase of 8s–12s a week on the existing county minima. The Ministry of Labour, by the Restriction of Engagements Order, prohibited employers in other industries from engaging existing agricultural workers, and it agreed to direct into farm work any industrial unemployed with suitable experience. (In fact few men could be found who fulfilled the treble qualification of having experience in agriculture and of being both unemployed and willing to move.) The new Minister of Agriculture, Mr Robert Hudson, later Lord Hudson plunged with characteristic energy into the problems of price policy.

COSTS AND PRICES

Hitherto discussions on agricultural prices had dealt with individual products considered in isolation. Whatever had happened to the costs of producing them, it had been assumed that a rather larger increase in prices was to be granted ; the increase in profits thus resulting would, it was hoped, encourage farmers to increase their output. The size of that incentive had been decided more by the bargaining power

of the different farming sections than by any rational calculation of priorities or of the cumulative changes in total profits
which resulted from individual price changes. In May 1940
it was found ' that the increased return per annum already
obtained by farmers would cover by more than £12 millions
their increased costs to date, plus the new increases in wages ;
nevertheless, the pledge to increase prices so as to match
increased costs would have to be fulfilled.' [1] On the existing
numbers employed it was calculated that the new minimum
wage would add £14·9 millions to total costs. But a new
instalment of £15 millions would, it was found, barely raise
the controlled prices of wheat, potatoes, sugar-beet and milk
to parity with those already established for oats, barley, pigs
and eggs ; to add anything to the prices of these less important
products, while bringing others into line, would involve adding a total not of £15 millions but of at least £20 millions to
farmers' profits.

But those responsible for the food production campaign
were at this stage more interested in psychology than in
costings. Whatever the merits of the existing scale of prices,
farmers had planned their production with it in mind, and to
alter its balance before the crops were sold might destroy that
confidence in the Government's intentions on which depended
farmers' willingness to invest their profits and their efforts in
greater output. Costs must not only be covered, but, it was
argued, must be seen to be covered by so substantial a margin
that no farmer would doubt his financial strength in the test-
ing years ahead. On these arguments a schedule of prices
was agreed which added some £35 millions to farmers' receipts,
and which largely perpetuated for the 1939–40 season the
existing price relationships. For the next season (the crops to
be sold in 1941–2 and the livestock sold in 1940–1) there was
to be a slight rearrangement of prices, giving a larger increase
for milk, potatoes and sugar-beet, and a smaller increase for
oats, feeding barley, fat cattle and pigs. And as a counter-
balance, the existing concession which allowed farmers to be
assessed for income tax not on their profits but on the basis

[1] Hancock, W. K. and Gowing, M. M., *British War Economy*, p. 160

of their rent was withdrawn from those rented at £300 or more. Two years later this limit was reduced to £100, and those beneath it were henceforth assumed to be earning at least three times their rent.

To this price settlement two additions were made later. The first, designed to reinforce the impact on farming psychology of the new price structure, was an announcement that the Government proposed to continue the existing sytem of guaranteed prices and of markets for the duration of the war and for at least one year after it. The second arose from the qualifying clause which accompanied the schedule of agricultural prices of 1940–1, the clause which declared these prices to be fixed subject to review in the event of substantial changes in the cost of production. The complex of mathematics, psychology and politics which lay in wait for those who 'adjusted prices to costs' had perhaps warned the administrators that the process should not be lightly undertaken. It seemed reasonable to hope that farm wages could now be stabilised at the revised level ; selling prices for fertilisers and feedingstuffs were largely under Government control, even though the costs of the imported ingredients were uncertain. Since the Ministry of Food now bought the greater part of the farming output and sold it in the retail market at controlled prices, it made little difference whether it subsidised the prices of fertilisers and of cattle cake or charged their full costs of acquisition and paid higher prices for the crops, fat stock and milk. In the autumn of 1940 the Government announced that the prices of fertilisers and feedingstuffs would be stabilised at their existing level irrespective of their costs.

Looking back on these related decisions from a distance of years, the fundamental points can be seen more clearly than they appeared in the dust of the conflict. A vast increase in production was now required from British agriculture, an industry characterised by 'increasing costs.' Making all allowance for the better use of scientific knowledge and for improvements in managerial efficiency, much of the increased production must come from the poorer land, giving lower yields at higher costs per ton. The conversion of grassland into arable involved expenditure by farmers on tractors and cultivating tools which might be redundant and almost value-less at the end of the war ; the first crop was often poor because of wireworm or of the general inexperience of cultivations. On all types of farms the sudden increase in wages upset the previous balance between costs of labour and costs of mechanisation, in a degree which was proportionate to the weight of labour costs in the total expenditure of each farm. With all these variables and with all the uncertainties abroad there was much to be said for the Government's declared policy of not paying the home producer ' the very minimum that is possible, but to give such a price as will encourage his further efforts.' [1] In the circumstances of 1940, when there was still under-farmed land, unemployed land girls and good supplies of fertilisers, generosity in farm prices could reasonably be expected to yield tangible results through intensified farming. Clearly, however, there was a limit to this process, set by the growing scarcity, in the conditions of total war, of all the factors of production—the scarcity of machinery and of men. A generosity which was perhaps justified in 1940 might be quite valueless in the conditions, say, of 1943.

This price settlement raised also two other matters of principle. At the time the Minister of Food made the statement quoted above, he was promptly asked whether the same argument about inducement to production applied to the payment of piece rates for workers on munitions. If farmers' profits had to be allowed to rise to such a level that no doubts should arise over the financing of the increased production, were not the coal-owners and coal-miners, and the firms and workers in the food trades equally entitled to similar generosity at the expense of the taxpayer ? And what then became of the threatened inflation, with its dangers of too much money chasing too few goods, goods that were becoming progressively fewer ?

And, secondly, it was surely unfortunate to continue for yet another season the unbalanced price structure which had

[1] House of Commons Debates, 8 Feb. 1940

resulted from the improvisations and emergencies of the first
winter of war.   Farmers were being asked to reduce the
numbers of sheep, pigs and hens in order to free land to produce crops for human consumption or for the dairy herd ;
yet the prices offered for these products, compared with the
pre-war level, were relatively higher than those of milk, wheat
or potatoes, products of the greatest importance in the years
of siege that lay ahead.   In June 1940 the price-fixing authorities seemed dangerously near to arguing that prices generally
must be raised to induce greater production, and must be
raised the most for the products whose output was planned
to fall ;   their wish to minimise financial hardship for the
specialist holdings entirely dependent on pigs and poultry
clashed sharply with the provision of price incentives appropriate to the future cropping of the great majority of farms.

THE NEW MEASURES

The starting-point of this long controversy over prices was
the decision of the new Government, headed by Mr Churchill,
that production of food would have to be greatly intensified.
In this task both prices and administration had a part to play.
The administrative framework established at the outbreak of
war had proved its worth in the winter of 1939-40 ;   the
members and officers of the Agricultural Executive Committees
had provided moral suasion, local leadership and technical
advice for the first ploughing campaign.   The new Minister
of Agriculture had to extend and strengthen this framework
in England and Wales and to infuse it with his own energy
and purposeful direction.

His first step was to ask the Farm Institutes which existed
in many counties to suspend their teaching after the summer
term and to lend their staffs to the Agricultural Executive
Committees as advisers on technical and scientific matters.
He also appointed a number of men distinguished in agricultural science, practice or administration as personal liaison
officers between himself and the committees.   Thus strength-
ened, the committees were asked to make, in the summer and

autumn of 1940, a quick survey of each farm in their respective areas, of its potentialities for further production and of the chief deficiencies, whether of equipment, machinery or management, which hindered the rapid realisation of these potentialities.[1]

The Minister urged on his committees the need for firmer measures upon those farmers whose deficiencies were mainly personal. Lack of cash or of credit could no longer be accepted as a sufficient excuse for inadequate cultivations or inferior grassland. The new prices gave to most farmers the assurance of a substantially increased income which would not only provide cash but also greater credit-worthiness. The committees could also, at their discretion, supply farmers with agricultural requisites—seeds, fertilisers, lime—with repayment by instalments from the monthly milk cheque or after harvest ; they could themselves, by agreement with the farmer, plough and cultivate his fields for him and again defer his payment until later. In default of agreement, the committees had powers to issue directions to any farmer specifying exactly what cultivations were to be executed in what manner at what times. And finally, the committees could recommend to the Minister that land held by a tenant or an owner-occupier who seemed incapable of putting it to proper use should be requisitioned ; it could then be farmed directly by the committees concerned or could be re-let to a tenant approved by them.

These powers to eject an occupier from his holding, with consequent loss both of employment and of home, naturally aroused misgivings among the farming community. And they were used fairly extensively. From September 1939 to March 1945 443,000 acres of agricultural land in England and Wales were requisitioned in this way, and tenancies of another 225,000 acres were terminated. But most of this area consisted of detached pieces of land—building plots, grazing fields, common grazings and derelict farms, and in Scotland indeed practically all the land requisitioned was deer forests and sheep grazings. There were, south of the Border, less than fourteen hundred

[1] This survey was repeated in more detail in 1941–3 and its main results have been published in *The National Farm Survey* (H.M.S.O. 1946).

cases in which compulsory acquisition involved a complete holding and its house,[1] a figure which must be compared with the 300,000 or so of farmers in England and Wales. In most of these evictions, local opinion supported the action of the Minister, but there were inevitably border-line cases in which sympathies were more equally divided. A complaint often heard in the House of Commons was the absence of any provision for appeal for a farmer threatened with eviction; the officers of the Executive Committee which recommended that action, the Land Commissioner who investigated the recommendation and the Civil Servant who finally signed the Order on behalf of the Minister were all parts of one entity, ' the Ministry of Agriculture,' so that counsel for the prosecution appeared to be also the judge and jury. On the other side the Minister argued that Executive Committees tended on the whole to show undue leniency towards inefficient farmers who were often pleasant neighbours; that the further delay necessarily involved in proceedings before a court of law meant so much less food produced. It was not until the passing of the Agriculture Act, 1947, that the power to appeal was formally conceded to farmers threatened with eviction.

By these measures the Agricultural Executive Committees became farmers themselves on a considerable scale in some English and Welsh counties. What they acquired was ' problem ' land—neglected, under-farmed, bush-covered, water-logged, or waterless, lacking buildings or roads. With such equipment as the Ministry could provide, with inexperienced staff and oddments in agricultural workers, the Committees tackled formidable problems of reclamation and rehabilitation, ranging from bog-oak in the Cambridgeshire fens to bracken on the Welsh hills. It is not surprising that they occasionally made mistakes in judgment and technique; that some of their methods proved more costly than the results justified. More important than these intermittent failures were the frequent successes in converting derelict land to efficient food production, and the examples thereby given to owners of similar land to do likewise in the national interest.

[1] House of Commons Debates, 29 March 1945

Drainage

The survey of farms in 1940 showed how frequently lack of drainage was the main handicap to increased output ; the English clays were more affected by water-logging than any other type of soil.   In the worst areas the problem required to be tackled at three levels :   the main rivers needed to be dredged and embanked, the minor streams to be cleared and deepened, and finally field ditches and drains to be repaired or installed.   The general overhaul in 1930 of the confusing medley of drainage authorities had enabled some progress to be made with the main watercourses, but the urgencies of war both suspended the major schemes and necessitated immediate measures for the improvement of farms and fields. Grants in aid for clearing minor streams and ditches and for the laying of tile and mole drains brought an activity unparalleled for a century ;   more than five million acres in England and Wales benefited during the years of war from drainage in some form or other, much of it done by farmers themselves, much executed by the Agricultural Executive Committees for land in their possession or on contract for farmers in their respective areas.[1]

Machinery

During these years the countryside became accustomed to the sight of cumbersome machinery working on some neglected ditch which was rapidly being converted from an over-grown, ineffective watercourse into a regular, clearly-cut channel with symmetrical sides of bare earth and a wide band of ' spoil ' spread along each bank.   These excavators and dredges were only the most conspicuous items in the supply of new machinery which poured on to British farms in the nineteen-forties, and whose organisation was a most important task for the Agricultural Departments.   The arrangements made with the Ford Motor Company in the spring of 1939 had enabled the Executive Committees to be equipped in

[1] Nicholson, H. H., ' Field Drainage and Increased Production,' *Journal R.A.S.E.*, 1948, vol. 109, p. 213

1939–40 with a modest number of tractors and cultivating implements, but the programme of intensified production adopted in the summer of 1940 required for its timely execution a vastly increased use of all forms of farm machinery.

For the first year of war the import of machinery was limited by the scarcity of dollars, though some useful purchases were made from Australia. The advent of Lend-Lease in March 1941 opened the doors to the huge production of the North American continent in which the Ministry of Agriculture promptly claimed a large share. What it especially needed, to supplement the output of the British manufacturers, were heavy tractors (the crawlers) for land reclamation and for the cultivation of the heavy clays ; disc harrows to break up the grassland ; binders and combine harvesters to speed up the great corn harvests planned for the years of siege ; and a host of minor implements—ploughs, drills, harrows, potato ridgers and diggers, as well as all the wheeled tractors that were available. The speed with which the Ministry organised the flow of these essential tools after 1940 was indeed fortunate, for the entry of the United States into a war that became ' global ' with the bombs on Pearl Harbour inevitably checked the expanding output of purely agricultural machinery. Whether in Britain, in Canada or in America, the allocation of machine tools, of raw materials and of skilled labour for the manufacture of tractors and ploughs was always subject to the overriding priorities for tanks and guns, for ships and shells and aircraft.

The Labour Problem

The responsibilities of the Agricultural Departments did not end with the provision of agricultural implements. There remained the provision of the men (and women) without whom that machinery would be useless. In the first flush of enthusiasm, the Minister in June 1940 called for 100,000 men to volunteer for agricultural work ; problems of employment, of housing in a countryside overflowing with evacuees were swept aside as minor hindrances. But the logic of events soon brought a more sober estimate of what would be available.

The idea that 100,000 men with previous agricultural experience could be found among the industrial unemployed quickly evaporated as the industrial unemployed, with or without a record of farm work, went into the armed services, or back to work in the steel mills, the munition factories and the ship-yards. By the spring of 1941 it was clear that the extra workers available for agriculture would be mainly women supplemented by conscientious objectors to military service and by such prisoners as the fortunes of war placed in British hands. Whatever the objection of many farmers to employing women, it was to the ' Land Girl ' that many of them turned from 1941 onwards to fill the place left by a departing con-script or to cope with the dairy and the tractor. Within two years of Dunkirk nearly 60,000 women and girls had thus been taken into the service of farming, and their numbers rose to a peak of more than 80,000 in 1943–4.

It was not only farmers who engaged these willing if inexperienced volunteers ; the Agricultural Executive Com-mittees rapidly became large employers of the Land Army. Urged by the Agricultural Departments to good works of land reclamation, of farming derelict fields, of drainage, the Committees found themselves committed to a vast experiment in the organisation of farm workers on a scale hitherto unknown. Instead of a personal relationship between a few men working alongside their employer with the minimum of formal regula-tion, the Committees had to develop methods of directing large numbers of primarily unskilled workers owning only a vague loyalty to an impersonal organisation. Their employees often lacked at the start the basic knowledge of agriculture which enabled them to understand the purpose and method of execution for each piece of work ; they did not know the necessary techniques for the jobs which followed each other in the course of the seasons, or the modifications required to meet the variations in soil and weather. The work was not only physically arduous ; much of it was monotonous and had to be done in unpleasant conditions by isolated groups of workers with little shelter for their midday picnic and no canteen to provide ' joint and two veg.' and a change of scene.

There was a great shortage of foremen sufficiently experienced to train novices, sufficiently articulate to explain the whys and wherefores and also willing to take responsibility for the minor details of organisation and discipline. The traditions of farming provided no assistance to these Committees struggling with problems of sick pay and of bad time-keeping ; of bad-weather employment for tens of workers ; of organising a steady succession of jobs which ranged from bush grubbing to beet singling, from potato picking to drainage, from the spraying of fruit trees to the catching of rats and rabbits. All these novel problems had to be solved by a process of trial, error and success.

As the Executive Committees became employers in a large way, the Agricultural Departments inevitably acquired heavy responsibilities in housing. 'The Land Girl' might find a home in the farm-house or in a nearby cottage ; but the tens of Land Girls employed by some Committees required hostels. And hostels, when provided from requisitioned mansions or by huts of the Ministry of Works, required matrons, orderlies, boiler men and, most essential of all, cooks. And of all scarce commodities, the scarcest during the war was the good plain cook who could provide from war-time rations sufficient (and sufficiently varied) sandwiches and two hot meals a day for growing girls spending eight hours a day on hard work in the open air.

Having sketched briefly the administrative framework within which agriculture was to operate during the war, some account must here be given of the corresponding changes in the distribution of food, which begins with the marketing of agricultural produce and ends with the delivery of the final result to retail shops. For the whole system of agricultural marketing was radically changed under the impact of war, and its corollary, food rationing.

BIBLIOGRAPHY

HANCOCK, W. K. and GOWING, M. M., *British War Economy* (H.M.S.O. 1949)

HURD, ANTHONY, *A Farmer in Whitehall* (Faber 1951)

House of Commons Debates, 1940, 1945

TRIST, P. J. O., *Land Reclamation* (Faber 1948)

BLOOM, A., *Farm in the Fen* (Faber 1944)

CHAPTER V

MARKETS, RATIONING AND PRICE CONTROL, 1940-4

THE experience of 1914–18 indicated that the primary feature of a war economy is scarcity. For food, scarcity in Britain arose from two causes. There was, firstly and most obviously, a reduction in the supply of many imported foods. Some of our suppliers (as of beet sugar) had become our enemies, so there was an actual shortage in allied countries ; later, ships were lost at such a rate that tonnage was not available to carry both the needed military supplies and the bulky foods. Secondly, demand rose, because money incomes increased, through higher wages and profits, more people in employment, longer hours of work. An increase in the effective demand for basic consumer goods, combined with a shrinking supply of them, led inevitably to rising prices, patchy distribution, social unrest and, eventually to price control and rationing.

THE THEORY OF RATIONING AND PRICE CONTROL

In normal times an increase in the demand for a commodity or a fall in its supply leads logically, other things remaining unchanged, to a rise in its price. That rise in price acts in two directions to restore equilibrium. Some would-be consumers, confronted with a higher price than they had expected, will decide to buy less, and thus the increase in demand will be mitigated. Higher profits to existing producers will in time induce a greater supply ; it will encourage the transfer of land, factories or labour into a now more profitable employment.

Such changes in the market for one product in times of peace have little bearing on the problems of the general scarcity of consumer goods in times of war. For many commodities, no rise in price, however drastic, can be allowed to induce a greater supply at the moment of greatest need. In

1917 it was unthinkable that resources of men and machinery should be diverted from the manufacture of ships, shells or guns to produce more furniture or fresh fruit. The employment of productive resources was dictated by military necessity, not by consumers' preferences. Secondly, during the last two years of the First World War the marked rise in the price of necessary foods threatened to limit demand in a manner which was socially unacceptable. If there had to be a fall in the total consumption of butter, milk, tea, meat and sugar there was no reason why that economy should be confined to the poorest people whose pre-war consumption was already too low for health.

And thirdly, the rise in food prices was found to have secondary consequences of great social and financial importance. The rising cost of necessities brought an irresistible pressure for higher wages in order to mitigate exactly that threatened fall in the already low standards of the poorest classes. Rising wages meant rising costs in agriculture, industry, transport and distribution ; rising costs implied rising prices for the final products, bought either by the consumer or by the Government which was the ultimate purchaser of the growing output of munitions and war supplies. Rising prices again led inexorably to further claims for higher wages and to further borrowing by the Government to fill the gap between expenditure and tax receipts. At the peak of the post-war inflation in 1920, wholesale prices and the average wage-rates of industrial workers were three times the pre-war level ; the cost-of-living index, partly stabilised by rationing and price control at the end of the war, rose to 250 per cent of its pre-war level. But prices had no sooner ceased to rise than they began to fall ; the subsequent deflation was even more rapid than the previous inflation, wholesale prices falling by half of their peak within eighteen months. Retail prices fell more slowly, and the process of reducing money wages led to a period of acute industrial strife and unrest. Price movements of this magnitude, it was clear, hampered the whole-hearted prosecution of a war and greatly embittered the difficult tasks of post-war reconstruction.

This experience drawn from the First World War led to a firm belief in the virtues of price control to be enforced from the beginning of any Second World War and not imposed after prices had already doubled. But price control by itself had proved to be ineffective. If supply was falling because imports had failed, or demand was rising because people had more money to spend, control of prices at a pre-war level could be positively harmful. An excess of demand over supply at the controlled price left distribution to the favour of the shopkeeper and the buying skill and black-market tendencies of the consumers. If the prices of basic foodstuffs were to be controlled there must be rationing of demand to secure 'fair shares' and efficient distribution ; if consumers were to be rationed, the Ministry of Food must be able to control supplies (whether home grown or imported) to ensure firstly that the ration was honoured, and secondly that there were no leaks into unauthorised channels. Price control implied some form of rationing ; rationing implied the control of markets and of supplies.

The improvised rationing schemes of 1917-19 were based on the allocation to each individual of a specified quantity, per week or per month, obtainable on the presentation of the appropriate coupon at the shop where the consumer was registered. On this basis, closely followed in the plans drawn up in 1936-9, 'rationing is a rigid, arithmetical and somewhat inhuman way of allocating the food of individuals ; it takes no account of individual tastes.' [1] It was only in a superficial sense that a uniform ration of fats or meat or sugar could be described as a policy of 'fair shares' ; as long as human beings differ in health, physique, tastes and customs, the possession of equal quantities of food has only indirect relationship with their personal wants. But strict rationing of food was essential in a state of siege, when social policy demanded the rough equalisation of hardship rather than the maximum of satisfaction.

Even on this basis some variation in the basic rations was

[1] House of Commons Debates, 18 July 1940, Parliamentary Secretary, Ministry of Food

recognised as unavoidable to meet such variations in physical needs as could be clearly ascertained. Special allowances for vegetarians and for sufferers from certain diseases were later extended to provide extra rations for expectant mothers, including a priority in milk supplies for them and also for young children. Should there not also be extra rations for those engaged in heavy manual work whose input of food might be expected to be above the average ? The physical need was recognised, but the administrative difficulties of defining ' heavy work ' proved insuperable ; the compromise included canteens for the ' heavy work ' industries whose workers, whether manual or clerical, benefited from extra rations, and a special cheese ration for agricultural workers who had no canteens and who often could not get home for their midday meal.

This was, however, a later development. The plans for rationing in a Second World War, drawn up in 1936-9, envisaged the immediate introduction of consumer rationing for an uncertain number of basic foods likely to be scarce—sugar, tea, fats, bacon, meat and possibly others such as cheese ; and a temporary limitation of their prices to the pre-war level until the mechanism of distribution had been brought under control in order to implement the rationing. It was expected that a few weeks—four to six—would suffice for this process after the signal to introduce rationing had been given. Falling prices on world markets during 1938 and the early months of 1939 induced a comfortable belief that there need be no appreciable rise in domestic prices on the outbreak of war, so that the task of authority could be limited to preventing purely speculative movements in the first few weeks of disturbed markets.

The Theory in Practice

At the outbreak of war the precautionary plans of the Food (Defence Plans) Department were rapidly put into effect by its logical successor, the Ministry of Food. Prices of the major foods were stabilised at the pre-war level ; the regis-tration of the general public—a necessary preliminary to con-

sumer rationing—took place at the end of September ; men
with experience in the food trades joined with Civil Servants
in organising the new forms of distribution which would be
required to implement the rationing schemes.

But the smooth working of these plans was rudely interrupted. In the first place, the decision to introduce consumer
rationing of the basic foods was delayed by the Cabinet ; it
was not until early in 1940 that butter, bacon, meat and
sugar were formally rationed ; two other important foods,
tea and margarine (with lard), were not added to the rationing scheme until July 1940. The administrators, inspired by
those who had improvised the rationing schemes in 1917-19,
had assumed that a well-organised rationing scheme should
begin before there was any signs of scarcity ; that it should
begin while stocks were ample, distribution normal and prices
under control. The politicians, impressed by the hardships
which inevitably followed the forcible restriction of the consumers' choice, disputed the need for rationing until scarcities
were imminent. While the argument proceeded, the control
of livestock prices foundered, for the reasons explained above.
The temporary maximum prices, imposed to steady the
markets for a few weeks while the Ministry of Food organised
its new method of meat distribution, became quite untenable
in the latter part of the autumn ; they were finally abandoned
just before Christmas 1939 and control was resumed, after an
interval, early in January 1940. The delay sacrificed also
the stores of sugar collected before the war. Hoarding began
even before war was declared ; the abrupt rise in sales above
the normal level quickly exhausted the stocks carried by the
trade on which depended the efficient working of retail distribution ; and by the time rationing was made effective there
had reappeared all the symptoms condemned in 1917—queues
outside shops that had sugar, complaints from those that had
no more, housewives accusing the shopkeepers of favouritism,
and the shopkeepers accusing the housewives of unpatriotic
hoarding.

A more serious problem had to be faced in this busy
autumn, when yet another of the pre-war assumptions about

the war was found to be unjustified. On most wholesale markets there was a sharp rise in prices at the end of August and throughout September ; this rise was accentuated in British markets by the devaluation of sterling in relation to the dollar and by the considerable costs of insurance against war risks. By December 1939 the index of wholesale prices compiled by the Board of Trade had risen by one-quarter of the level recorded in the previous summer, and it was still rising ; the upward trend in wholesale prices caused, in the first four months of war, a 12 per cent increase in the index of retail prices compiled by the Ministry of Labour—the ' cost-of-living ' index. Was this the beginning of that ' inflationary spiral ' that had dominated the economics of the First World War ? Would this rise in prices, itself the signal for lowered consumption, lead irresistibly to higher wages, in order to prevent the restriction from falling unfairly on the poorest of the wage earners ?

One aspect of the problem was faced in November, when it was found that the Ministry of Food could not sell at the existing maximum prices the feedingstuffs imported after the outbreak of war without incurring a heavy loss. Should these prices be raised to correspond with the new level of costs ? It was argued, with some force, that a rising price level for imported feedingstuffs would reinforce the need to increase their production at home ; scarcity plus dearness might have more effect on farmers' psychology in this matter than scarcity alone. Where scarcity could be mitigated by suitable action there was much to be said for emphasising it ; and feeding-stuff prices were in fact raised, both in November 1939 and again early in 1940, to keep pace with the rising costs of acquisition. But a general rise in the retail prices of food could scarcely be regarded as a stimulus to the provision of substitutes ; there is no substitute for food. The arguments for and against a general rise in food prices, as distinct from feedingstuff prices, turned largely on the question of inflation, its causes and cures.

The history of the First World War showed that rising food prices provided one main reason for claiming higher wages, which in turn involved higher costs and higher prices. To keep down these prices, by rationing, price control and by direct subsidies, would largely remove that particular irritant. Yet there was no guarantee that wages would remain stable even if all retail prices were held indefinitely at their pre-war level. In conditions of total war there were plenty of other reasons why money incomes would increase faster than the supply of goods—longer hours, more people in work, more people in the higher paid jobs and, most important of all, the absolute scarcity of manpower which developed not indeed in this autumn of 1939 but after the autumn of 1941. If money incomes would rise in any case, would not a higher price level for necessities siphon off some of the excess of purchasing power and prevent worse symptoms of inflation in other markets?

Both arguments had force, but in the winter of 1939–40 the weight of opinion was in favour of preventing any further rise in food prices in the hope, if not of preventing increases in money incomes, at least of mitigating them. Government expenditure in the form of food subsidies was judged to have less immediate effects in creating inflation than expenditure on higher wages to munition workers and coal miners. At the end of the year it was agreed that the Exchequer should ' temporarily ' refund to the Ministry of Food any loss incurred on selling at existing retail prices future supplies of necessities ; prices of ' luxury ' foods, it was implied, should be left un-controlled. It was on this basis that retail milk prices were stabilised for the first three months of 1940, while prices to producers were raised by 2d–3d a gallon to cover the recently increased costs of feedingstuffs.

This decision coincided in time with that limited introduc-tion of consumer rationing mentioned earlier, a coincidence which gave to the Government policy an appearance of coherent intention which perhaps it hardly deserved. For the next development in prices at once called in question the basis of these ' temporary ' subsidies, and their relation to nutritional needs.

Practice Perfected

In June 1940 the whole schedule of prices paid to British farmers for their products was substantially raised ; in addition, the distributors of milk were claiming an increase in their margin to compensate for rising costs. How much, if any, of these price rises should be reflected in rising retail prices ? Was the Government to stabilise indefinitely the retail prices of the principal foods, a commitment which might involve subsidies amounting to hundreds of millions of pounds ? Was there not something to be said for differential prices, some scheme whereby basic necessities could be made cheaply available to the poorest classes while passing on the general rise in costs to those more able to afford them ?

Milk was a particularly important case, because of its nutritional importance. Pre-war surveys showed how inadequate was its consumption among the poorest classes whose large families at one and the same time needed milk and provided the chief reason for their inability to buy it. If milk prices were to be raised something should be done to ensure that mothers and children would still have at least their pre-war supplies and if possible more. There was an existing scheme for supplying cheap milk to schoolchildren, which had been partially disrupted by the evacuation ; local authorities also had little-used powers to provide milk, at reduced prices, for mothers and babies attending welfare clinics. A month of activity produced, on the morrow of Dunkirk, a social welfare scheme inconceivable in less heroic days. Expectant mothers, nursing mothers and babies, irrespective of status and income, were to obtain up to one pint of milk a day at the specially reduced price of 2d a pint (or free in necessitous cases) ; the ' non-priority consumer ' (one of the less happy definitions of food rationing) would henceforth pay the old retail price plus another $\frac{1}{2}$d a pint for what milk remained.

This compromise over milk prices left the major points of price policy still unsettled ; few commodities were suitable for differential prices in this way. Confronted with the uncertainty over future costs and supplies, the Government decided in the autumn of 1940 that the ' cost-of-living index ' should be stabilised at its existing level, in the hope of mitigating the pressure for higher wages. Food subsidies, on an indefinite scale, were therefore to be permanent. The decision implied that prices of ' luxury ' foods, those not in the cost-of-living index, might be allowed to rise ; indeed it was at one time suggested that a profit might be made on them in order to offset the subsidies. But whatever might be the views of administrators, the general public certainly did not regard as ' luxuries ' such things as canned salmon, tinned fruit, biscuits, breakfast cereals and onions, which were not included in the cost-of-living index because they were not generally bought by the working classes in 1904, when the index originated. Imports of such everyday articles fell rapidly in the latter half of 1940, and their prices rose sharply under the impetus of increasing demand, increasing distributive costs, and falling supply. At the end of the year the Ministry of Food brought almost all edible articles whether luxuries or not into the net of price control.

The immediate result was another lesson in the economics of total war. At the controlled price demand exceeded supply, and the most favoured articles ' went under the counter ' ; wholesale traders, in an attempt to keep down costs, sold all their supply in the areas nearest to the source ; the large inland towns were suddenly deprived of eggs, fish, cheese and tomatoes, while villages lacked breakfast cereals and tinned foods. There was only one satisfactory cure, the direct rationing of demand to the level of the restricted supplies, coupled with such control of distribution as would enable the ration to be met.

The rationing of the basic foods—meat, sugar, fats—implied the guarantee to each consumer of a certain quantity each week. Such an arrangement was impracticable for the host of minor commodities which provide both variety to the diet and a considerable if not weighty part of the intake of calories. In the course of 1941 the administrators devised a system of ' points ' rationing derived partly from what they knew of German methods and partly from economic theory. The foods were given two prices, one in cash and one in points ; each consumer (presumably in possession of well-earned cash) could spend each month a prescribed number of ' points ' ; the grand total of ' points ' issued was adjusted to equal the points value of the expected monthly supply of all rationed goods ; the ' points ' value to be given to each food was chosen in the hope of equating its ' points ' demand with its expected supply.

It was extraordinarily difficult to judge without any previous experience at what price, in points per tin, consumers would buy exactly those quantities of salmon, syrup and biscuits which were likely to be available. The initial ' points price ' of syrup was fixed too low ; there remained a shortage of syrup (because demand exceeded supply), while salmon and sardines decorated the shop windows. Raising the points price of syrup cured this particular irritant, but that step involved the reduction in the points value of some other food in order to maintain the equality in the grand total of points sold and offered ; and only experience could show what adjustment was required. In spite of these and other problems in administration, the points rationing scheme was an undoubted success ; it did succeed in distributing a varying supply of supplementary foods among the civilian population with a rough measure of justice.

Even this extension of rationing could not cope with the problems of some perishable foods with a highly seasonal production. A ration of tomatoes was impossible when no-one knew how many tomatoes would be ready for sale in any week. Fish provided a similar problem. For such foods the Ministry could only ensure that wholesalers in each district had a fair share of total supplies, and then leave the rest to the distributive trades and the consumers.

CONTROL OF DISTRIBUTION

Price control and food rationing involved the control of food supplies at some stage in the distributive process. The

Ministry of Food had two tasks in this field ; to ensure that the consumers got rations every week, whatever the weather or the blitz ; and to ensure that no controlled foodstuffs leaked by unauthorised channels into an unregulated black market. In this double task the Ministry was much helped by a fact which politicians were apt to deplore—the high proportion of British food supplies derived from imports. The experience of continental countries in two wars has showed how difficult it is to implement food rationing when supplies have to be drawn in small units from millions of producers most of whom are easily within the reach of large urban markets. With the exception of milk, potatoes, eggs and vegetables, the major part of the foodstuffs required in Britain were delivered in shiploads at the ports whence their distribution could be easily controlled. It is not accidental that the rationing of eggs (and of potatoes in the post-war season of 1947-8) were among the least successful of the Ministry's schemes for ' fair shares at fixed prices.'

The task of the Ministry of Food from 1940 onwards was to keep the British people adequately and fairly fed with the minimum expenditure of ships, land and manpower. And the first price-control orders issued by the Ministry, early in September 1939, exhibited one continuing feature of the war-time economy—a drastic simplification in grades, qualities and varieties. The National Mark Schemes devised by the Agricultural Departments to improve the quality of home-grown produce, the heavily advertised brands of margarine or bacon, Canterbury lamb from New Zealand and Wiltshire sides from Denmark all disappeared. Meat was meat ; eggs were either home produced or imported with no guarantee over their internal development ; apples became just apples, whatever their variety, shape, flavour or degree of infestation with scab. The housewife put her family's books on the shop counter, and was handed the week's rations with no questions asked or answered about preference, origin or quality.

One result of this simplification was undoubtedly to penalise the producer of first-quality foods. He not only lost his contacts with his market ; he very often lost as well his usual premium over the average market price. Scottish producers of well-finished beef carcases, the growers of early maturing lamb and the producers of milk with high fat content were all penalised in this general levelling of quality and of variety to suit the economical management of food rationing.

The general principle of the Ministry of Food was to appoint, as its authorised agents, the principal firms and persons operating in each trade at the outbreak of war. Through these authorised agents the Ministry became the legal buyer of most products at an early stage in the distributive process. By the end of the first year of war, the Ministry was buying in overseas markets (and often from overseas Governments) the foods it needed ; it retained possession sometimes right down to the sale at fixed prices to the retailer ; sometimes the product (wheat for instance) was sold to a processor who was bound to sell to the next stage in the distributive process only to authorised agents at controlled prices. It made little practical difference whether the trade handled the foods for fixed margins as agents of the Ministry or whether they were the legal owners selling at one fixed price what they had bought at another fixed price ; the different procedures might cause headaches to the Ministry's accountants but the general method of physical control was the same.

Potatoes, for instance, had to be sold at controlled prices to an authorised agent who sold them to his usual customers— another wholesaler or a retail shop—at prescribed prices. The Ministry of Food itself did not normally buy potatoes. It did, however, undertake to buy potatoes for which a market could not otherwise be found ; from 1941 onwards it also bought all the output of certain varieties known to keep well in order to provide a reserve against that uncomfortable gap in April, May and June each year before the arrival of the new potatoes. Any stocks so acquired which were not needed in the retail market were resold to farmers for stockfeed at much reduced prices. Area potato officers (many of them taken over from the suspended Potato Marketing Board) arranged these purchases and assisted in the smooth distribution of the crop from the farms to the nearest markets.

A more complicated procedure was required for the trade in fat stock, which had to be adapted to the requirements of meat rationing. Established auction markets became collecting centres ; each farmer was required to sell all his fat stock at his nearest market and to give twelve days' notice of what he proposed to sell. This notice enabled the officials firstly to make at each centre the necessary arrangements for transport and slaughter, and secondly to adjust the incoming supplies of imported meat so as to provide for each region the required total of meat for the weekly ration. At each collecting centre, the sheep and cattle were weighed and graded by a representative of the farmers, an auctioneer or dealer, and a representative of the butchers ; the owner of the stock was paid the current fixed price for that grade on the live weight for cattle and the estimated dead weight for sheep. There was a drastic reduction in the number of slaughter-houses in operation, and most of the small privately owned ones in rural districts were closed early in 1940 ; the urban slaughter-houses continued as agents of the Ministry of Food which remained the owner of the meat until it reached the retail shop. Butchers were grouped in geographical regions and agents from each group were responsible for taking delivery of meat (whether home killed or imported) and for dividing it among their members in proportion to buying permits which recorded the number of registered consumers. These methods of distribution were required in order to ensure the punctual arrival of a certain quantity of meat to match the consumers' ration ; the system was not designed to supply what consumers wanted or preferred, and there was a considerable volume of complaint over the distributive uniformity which ignored local preferences and dietary customs. Scottish housewives, brought up on Scottish beef, were offered Argentine mutton to take or leave ; London families who always had Canterbury lamb found their Sunday joint reduced to an unknown cut from an old cow. All that was claimed was that the method of distribution did succeed with remarkable efficiency in supplying each week from imports and from British farms a prescribed amount of animal protein to every consumer, which was all that was required in totalitarian war.

More tricky problems in administration were provided by eggs. Just before the war British farms supplied about half of the total commercial supply of eggs, in competition mainly with farmers in northern Europe. The events of 1940 extinguished the imports of eggs, and it was not until 1943 that supplies of dried egg in tins arrived in substantial quantities from North America. With higher money incomes and the shortage of other foods there was no doubt that potential demand would increase from 1940 onwards ; but supply had been halved, and even home production was expected to fall as cereals were diverted from poultry to the consumption of humans and of dairy cows.

The Ministry of Food made a valiant effort to bring eggs into the framework of rationing and price control. As part of the general policy of stabilising the cost-of-living index, the retail price of eggs was substantially reduced in the summer of 1941 in spite of higher prices to producers. All poultry keepers with more than twenty-five hens had to sell their eggs at the controlled price to authorised packing stations from whence they were redistributed to wholesalers and retail shops at prices which enabled them to sell to their registered consumers at the prescribed retail price. Those with less than the prescribed number of hens might sell direct to anyone, but legally the sale had to take place at the retail price which was usually below the price obtained at the packing station. No-one, and certainly not the Ministry, ever thought that the scheme was wholly satisfactory. Eggs are small, portable, need no processing and are a most desirable adjunct to a restricted diet ; if a consumer who was willing to pay more than the maximum price came into contact with a producer with eggs to sell it is only reasonable to suppose that a sale was effected. But the Ministry's efforts did succeed in securing at least some eggs for the large towns.

At the outbreak of war there were nine Boards established under the Agricultural Marketing Acts concerned with the marketing of four products—potatoes, hops, bacon pigs (three Boards) and milk (four Boards). Of these, the Marketing Boards for potatoes and for pigs were suspended in the autumn of 1939 as inappropriate to war-time policy. The Hops Board continued, as before, to negotiate the annual price for hops sold to the brewers and maltsters; because there were no imports of hops after 1940 and a rising thirst, the Board rapidly found itself in the happy position of selling on a rising market.[1] But hops are only of minor importance in British agriculture and the operations of the Hops Board are of less general interest than those of the Milk Marketing Boards, which controlled the most valuable single product sold by British farmers.

For some time after the outbreak of war (and for some functions throughout the whole decade), the Milk Marketing Boards continued to operate as selling agencies for their dairy farmers. Their first concern was to safeguard the interests of the producers by obtaining a price for them which at least maintained, and if possible improved, the pre-war relationship between costs and returns. But by the end of 1939 costs had risen through higher prices, interrupted supplies of feedingstuffs and an upward trend in wages; the average pool price, compounded from the prices received for milk sold liquid and for manufacture, tended to fall because evacuations of towns and of schools reduced the volume of milk bought at the liquid price. Some improvement in manufacturing prices was obtained from condensers and chocolate makers, but the efforts of the Boards to enforce higher retail prices clashed with the declared intention of the Government to stabilise 'temporarily' the prices of basic foodstuffs. As noted above, the immediate result of this conflict of interests was a 'temporary' subsidy from the Exchequer, by which the existing average pool prices paid to dairy farmers were raised by 2d–3d per gallon above those paid in the same months of the preceding year, while retail prices remained unchanged. This 'temporary' break in the

[1] *Report of the Second Reorganisation Commission for Hops*, M.A.F. Economic Series, No. 47 (H.M.S.O. 1947)

link which previously kept retail and wholesale prices in alignment proved in the event to be permanent, outlasting at any rate a decade of war and post-war changes. The price paid to dairy farmers for their milk was henceforth fixed by some reference to the costs of the expected supply and was completely divorced from the prices paid either by milk distributors or milk manufacturers, themselves now selling their products at controlled prices. The Milk Marketing Boards had no longer to negotiate prices with these customers but to argue with the representatives of the Government departments most concerned—the Treasury and the Ministries of Food and Agriculture.

This new relationship was formally expressed in two regulations under the Defence Act which changed the basic responsibility of the Boards to their members, the registered dairy farmers. From the middle of 1940 the Boards were required to exercise their powers derived from the Agricultural Marketing Acts in accordance with any directions given to them by the Ministry of Food. Two years later, when it became necessary to impose milk rationing, all existing contracts in England and Wales for the sale of milk between farmer and distributor were cancelled ; the Milk Marketing Board became the first buyer of all milk sold wholesale ; it re-sold the milk to the Ministry of Food which paid for it such a sum as was required by the Marketing Board to pay to producers the prescribed prices ; the Milk Division of that Ministry was then responsible for the transport of milk to its next stage, the wholesale dairy or the manufacturer. This clear distinction in function and responsibility was, to the outsider, somewhat confused because the Milk Division of the Ministry of Food was largely recruited from the experts of the Milk Marketing Board ; the same man might appear one day as an official to argue with farmers over details of milk disposal ; and on the next as a representative of the registered dairy farmers to argue with officials over prices and costs. The position of the Milk Marketing Boards themselves was more than a little illogical ; they retained the annual election of members, the annual general meeting and presentation of accounts prescribed by their constitution as democratically controlled bodies under the Agricultural Marketing Acts ; yet during the war they exercised their functions as directed by the Ministry of Food, with Ministerial responsibility for their acts and omissions. But the illogical arrangement worked, and there were worse things than illogicality to worry about during the siege of Tobruk, the fall of Singapore, and the Battle of the Atlantic.

Over the whole field of food distribution the Ministry of Food thus exercised a regulatory and directing interest. From the initial purchase of supplies, whether at home or abroad, the agents of the Ministry organised the transport (by land or sea), the storage, processing and packing and the final delivery of the edible article to the housewives officially described as holders of ration books. The stabilisation policy of the Government implied that after 1941 a subsidy had to be injected into the distributive process for the major foods so that retail prices should remain unchanged, whatever the rise in the price originally paid or in the costs of the intermediate processes. Thus by the end of the war egg-packing stations paid to the farmers higher prices for eggs received than they charged for the eggs sold to wholesalers or retailers ; the packing stations themselves were remunerated for their services by a fixed commission on all eggs handled.

The control of distributive costs and margins for all major foods was a highly complex matter. The trade in each product had its own customs and weights, its own peculiarity in processing, storage and transport, its own methods of finance, its own combination of importer and wholesaler or of merchant and dealer. The milk trade, for instance, handled a huge volume of a highly perishable liquid to be delivered, after elaborate but rapid processing, to millions of doorsteps every morning. It had a mechanism of exceptional diversity, ranging from the producer-retailer who sold the milk provided by his own cows, to a combination of a feeder depot, a main supply depot, a town wholesaler with pasteurising and bottling plant and finally a retailer. The administration of food supplies did not end, therefore, with the production of more food ; once grown, the products had to be collected from the farms for dispatch to the consumer along recognised channels at controlled prices in regular quantities. Many tangled problems in control and rationing, in costs, prices and margins, were involved, problems which were often ignored both by farmers and by housewives at opposite ends of the chain of distribution.

BIBLIOGRAPHY

Journal, Agricultural Economics Society, December 1945

HAMMOND, R., *Food*, vol. i. 'The Growth of Policy' (H.M.S.O. and Longmans, 1951)

CHAPTER IV

FOOD FOR THE SIEGE, 1940-2

The Nutritional Basis

The last chapter but one gave a brief account of the administrative measures adopted from 1940 onwards to speed the mobilisation of agricultural resources. We must now return to the summer of 1940 to trace the use made of these resources as they were deployed. It was clear that Britain would need more home-grown food, partly to ease the strain placed on our financial resources by overseas purchases, partly as an insurance against the loss of ships now threatened by submarines and aircraft based on the coast of northern Europe from Norway to Brittany. But what kind of food was most urgently needed ? How could the population in these besieged islands be adequately fed, with the minimum of resources in land, labour and imports ?

Answers to these questions were provided by the scientific advisers to the Ministry of Food. They calculated that all the nutritional needs of the nation, expressed in calories, proteins, fats, minerals and vitamins, could theoretically be provided by a diet of wholemeal bread, oatmeal, fats, milk, potatoes and vegetables. Wheat and fats would have to be imported ; but all the other foods in this list, the scientists thought, could be produced at home to meet the needs of the whole population. The function of livestock for such a diet was to convert into meat the inedible by-products of intensified cropping such as straw, chat potatoes and sugar-beet tops, and to graze such land as could not be ploughed. The small quantity of meat thus produced, together with miscellaneous imports, would provide a modicum of variety in a diet which the scientists themselves admitted to be totally unlike that commonly found among an industrial population.

Such a diet was not indeed practical for a number of

reasons.   Oat-milling capacity for instance was quite in-adequate to supply the quantities of oatmeal proposed ; and if circumstances had demanded such drastic austerity in diet, its effect on morale might have been disastrous.   But the importance of these views lay, not in the scientific calculations of what was theoretically possible, but in the direction they imparted to the immediate plans for feeding the people. Imports and production need no longer be planned merely to maintain the normal diet ; with scientific approval, changes in that diet could be made in order to provide the same nutrients with less resources, to provide more cereals and vegetables, less meat and fruit.

The corresponding changes could now be planned for British agriculture.   A second ploughing campaign was to bring another $2\frac{1}{4}$ million acres under the plough for the harvest of 1941.   Enough land was to be planted with potatoes to provide all the British public would eat even at the lowest yield experienced in the last decade ; sugar-beet was to be produced up to the limit set by the existing capacity of the beet factories ; selected districts were to expand greatly their acreage of vegetables (and especially of tomatoes and carrots) in order to supply the vitamins formerly derived from imported fruit and vegetables.   For the rest, in the autumn of 1940 the Government was unwilling to commit itself too closely to production programmes for cereals or livestock.   There might be, indeed there probably would be, an intensified attack on the Atlantic traffic, but one immediate result of the occupation of Europe had been the arrival of ships and cargoes destined for now blockaded ports.   Temporarily, therefore, there was an improvement in imports which inevitably intensified the un-willingness of the Government to force upon farmers radical and unpopular changes.   The scientists might urge the immediate slaughter of pigs and poultry, of lowland sheep and beef cattle, in order to free land to grow crops for direct human consumption.   But more aware than their advisers of the technical problems of agriculture, the Government only issued warnings.   Farmers must not depend, over the coming winter, on regular supplies of imported feedingstuffs ; each farm must support its livestock to a greater degree from its own fields while giving due weight to the need for human foods in the form of wheat, potatoes and vegetables and, especially, milk.

Indeed, in the autumn of 1940 the Ministry of Food was more embarrassed by the efforts of the farmers to reduce their livestock than by the scientists' fears of their undue perseverance in animal husbandry. As noted in Chapter II, the effect of smaller supplies of imported feedingstuffs in the first year of war was to delay the slaughter of many animals until they had been fattened off the summer grass. The flood of these marketings, combined with the reduction in breeding stocks of sheep and pigs, overwhelmed the slaughtering facilities of the Ministry in September and October and provoked a controversy over livestock policy which continued during most of the second year of war.

LIVESTOCK AND FEEDINGSTUFFS

There were indeed those who argued for a variety of reasons that this drastic reduction in lowland sheep and cattle was undesirable and should be discouraged. Some maintained that the British public was carnivorous, and that morale might be badly shaken if the meat ration fell below the customary level. It was an opinion which was inevitably overborne by the weight of expert advice from the nutritionists and by the logic of events ; a sudden run of sinkings along the South American route sent the weekly meat ration down to 1s early in 1941, and yet morale was not immediately or visibly broken. A more serious contention was the probable effect on the production of food crops or the loss of livestock. For 150 years the combination of crops with stock had been the dominating feature of British agriculture ; the by-products of the corn, supplemented with roots, forage crops and imported concentrates were fed to sheep and cattle to provide the dung to put on the roots to grow not only roots but also, in due rotation, wheat, barley, oats and potatoes. Some agricultural experts, taking fright at the size of the autumn slaughterings, were quick to emphasise the importance of 'muck' in maintaining crop yields on arable land, and strongly opposed the further dispersal of flocks and herds.

But in the winter of 1940–1 the weight of opinion was on the other side, in favour of still fewer livestock. The value of 'muck,' it was felt, could be overrated. Enterprising farmers between the wars had showed that even light land could produce high yields without recourse to the traditional yarded cattle or folded sheep whose direct costs in labour and feeds exceeded any probable cash returns. Whether these systems of farming, which depended largely on fertilisers, could be widely extended was a debatable point, but rising wages and the growing scarcity of shepherds and stockmen were encouraging that trend. And secondly, the increase which was required in the volume of food grown for human consumption could at this stage be most rapidly obtained by increasing the area under approved crops at the expense of that under forage crops. On arable lands any appreciable reduction in yields caused by a shortage of 'muck' would be outweighed by the extra output of potatoes or grain obtained from fields which normally would be growing roots or green crops, while much of the newly ploughed grassland could take several crops of corn and potatoes before its humus content need cause anxiety. Indeed, farmers had shown by their action in the autumn of 1940 their realisation that livestock in pre-war numbers were a hindrance to the cropping programme that lay before them. But as the level of sinkings rose in the winter and the level of imports fell, it was argued that the slaughter of livestock should proceed still more rapidly, and probably more rapidly than most farmers realised.

The problem was one of degree and of timing. By the end of 1940 it was clear that hardly any imported feedingstuffs would be available in 1941. Eight million tons of imported cereals and cake had been struck off the menu for farm animals, which now consisted of home-grown fodder, milling offals and cattlecake, a by-product of the oilseed industry. There was a grave danger that farmers, unwilling to deplete the flocks and herds which represented million of pounds of invested

capital, would try to maintain too many animals in relation
to the still falling supply of concentrates available, so that the
livestock population would be appropriate to last year's feed
supplies rather than to next year's. The bulky home-grown
forage—straw, hay, roots and the like—would no doubt keep
the animals alive, but the output of meat and milk from
animals starved of their grain and cattle-cake might be
lamentably low. The farmer who in the First World War
was fined for giving bread to his cows had much public
sympathy when he declared, ' Well, I'll tell you straight, my
cattle is going to have something.' [1] As the rapid fall in milk
yields then showed, his dilemma arose because the number
of livestock had not been reduced in step with the drastic fall
in total food supplies which required the use of cereals to keep
humans from immediate starvation rather than to supply
them, through the mechanism of a dairy herd, with milk. To
a considerable extent, therefore, the number of farm animals
(and especially of pigs and hens which cannot cope with bulky
crops) had to be adjusted to the future supply of concentrates
and not merely to the supply of total feedingstuffs ; yet it was
also desirable to have enough cattle to convert into meat (and
farmyard manure) the by-products of arable farms and the
grass on the unploughable land. Some reduction in feeding
standards had thus to be accepted in making this adjustment ;
with a higher proportion of bulky feeds in each animal's diet,
the process of fattening would inevitably be slower and some
decline in the highest milk yields was bound to occur. But it
was important that this limited adjustment in the type and
quality of diet should not take the form of slow starvation for
most animals, because the change in their numbers had lagged
seriously behind the trend in the supplies of feed available for
them.

The second and equally important reason had a more
involved logic. The Government wanted more crops for
direct human consumption—wheat, potatoes, sugar-beet,
vegetables and the like. If there was at any time a sudden
interruption to the supply of food from overseas, the deficiency

[1] Beveridge, Sir W. H., *British Food Control*, p. 239 (O.U.P. 1928)

could also be met, temporarily, by drawing on the 'dual purpose' crops, such as oats, barley and pulse, which could fairly easily be converted direct into human food. (Oatcakes, barley bannocks, 'pease pudding hot and pease pudding cold' had fed many of our forefathers.) But these crops would not be available for such use in a crisis, say in a late spring, if they had already been consumed by farm animals over the winter. And the need to keep animals alive when the merchant could supply nothing for them would be a strong inducement to many farmers to grow fodder crops on land that could without harm grow crops for humans.

These considerations led to official propaganda in favour of still fewer livestock. Farmers were repeatedly warned that they must not rely on purchased cereals to feed their pigs and poultry, whose numbers should be steadily reduced to the level at which they could be supported from by-products of crops grown on the farm. They were asked to cull drastically their herds of beef cattle and of dairy cows to get rid of the poorest animals, so that the keep available should be used to the best purpose ; and in June the Ministry of Food adjusted its prices so as to provide temporarily higher prices for lean animals. Whether this campaign had any effect it is difficult to decide, for at the end of 1940 there developed a severe outbreak of foot-and-mouth disease in Eire. As a result imports of store cattle and of dairy heifers from Ireland were prohibited for almost a year, and this loss (amounting over the whole period to some 500,000 beasts) accounted for the decline compared with the previous year of 250,000 cattle in the June 1941 census for Great Britain. Numbers of sheep had also fallen over this period by more than four million, and the number of breeding sows, reflecting the future intention of pig farmers, had been halved. The statistics also showed a relative increase in the numbers of the older fattening animals. Can it be said that this adjustment was satisfactory ? That no crops were used for livestock which could with advantage have been converted to human consumption ?

There are two indications that the reduction in livestock did not proceed quite as fast as was nationally desirable. In supplies had to be procured from North America in a hurry, despite the shipping shortage, which fortunately was less severe then than in the previous winter. But the deficiency showed how strained was the supply of feedingstuffs in spite of the smaller numbers of stock and in spite of the animal rationing scheme introduced in February 1941 and discussed below. It is tempting therefore to conclude that the Government ought to have resorted earlier to more drastic measures, that it should have tried to telescope into eighteen months or two years that decline in numbers of sheep and pigs which continued for nearly three years.

The Ministry of Food would also have welcomed a much more even flow of livestock to market ; the animals which it refused for lack of facilities in September 1940 and eventually slaughtered in October, and those which were sold at the smaller but still marked peak in the autumn of 1941, would have been of greater value in March 1941 when the meat ration was down to 1s per head per week. It might be argued that this temporary 'bonus' in meat supplies, the 'reserve of meat on the hoof' provided by the dispersal of flocks and herds, should be entirely regulated by the needs of the consumer, but such an argument ignores the peculiarities of livestock production. Fat stock cannot be 'stored.' If sold substantially before they are fattened, the yield of meat is low, and that obtained is mainly of a quality for sausages rather than for the Sunday joint. To hold them after they are reasonably ready for market wastes food which is being used largely to add fat and not meat. And if the supply of concentrated feeds is falling rapidly and farmers are suddenly forced back on to home-grown fodder, the rate of slaughter is closely determined by the seasonal variations in the supply of grass. An accentuated autumnal peak in slaughterings, combined with marketings below the usual level in the first half of the year, thus seems an inevitable result of the process of adjusting livestock numbers to the exigencies of total war ; it occurred in 1916-17 as well as in 1940-1.

And a second point may also be noticed here. As long as substantial areas of permanent grassland are being ploughed each winter for crop production, the supply of winter fodder is lessened by the loss of second-cut hay and autumn and early spring grazing. But once the arable acreage has reached its peak, the loss of grass is partly counterbalanced by the increased supply of tail corn, straw, chat potatoes, the tops and pulp from sugar-beet and the cleaning crops grown in rotation. A close adjustment of livestock numbers to falling feed supplies might therefore involve at some time the slaughter of breeding stock which, if kept alive over another winter, could be adequately supported, with their progeny, on those by-products of crops grown for human consumption.

The relationship between livestock and their fodder is in fact highly complex, and the authorities were surely wise in leaving to the judgment of each farmer the final decision on the number and types of animals which his holding could reasonably support in conditions of war. Experience during the war showed for instance that many, perhaps most, farms understocked their grass in times of peace ; with better controlled grazing more beasts were successfully maintained than had been the usual custom. The Agricultural Executive Committees had indeed powers to issue directions to farmers on such matters ; but these legal sanctions were rarely used, and then only to enforce the production of a reasonable quota of priority crops such as wheat, potatoes or vegetables.

The Rationing of Feedingstuffs

The threat of food shortages led logically to price control and rationing, described in the last chapter ; and the shortage of imported feedingstuffs for animals induced a livestock rationing scheme in 1940-1. (Price control had been applied since the early weeks of war.)

The need for some such mechanism for distributing the limited supply of cattle cake and of coarse grains had been recognised in 1939-40, but nothing much had been done. There was in the first place the appalling complexity of the task and the lack of any previous experience. Animal rationing had indeed been contemplated in 1918, but the end of that war had saved the first Ministry of Food from risking its

reputation in so wide an extension of its work. In the inter-
vening years the number of farm animals had increased
together with their dependence on imported grains. And in
the second place, it was thought that a serious shortage of
feedingstuffs would be temporary; when the harvest of 1940
had been gathered in, the greater production of fodder would
surely fill much of the gap left by the substantial but not yet
drastic fall in imported supplies. And so no plans were
made until the Battle of Britain was being fought and won,
and the rate of sinkings in the Atlantic showed how few ships
would be available for the carriage of animal feeds in 1941.
And as milk consumption rose steadily after the introduction
of the National Milk Scheme and as milk supplies were
noticeably falling, it became imperative for dairy cows to
have first call on such supplies as were available.

The basis of the scheme, as first introduced, was the number
of cattle, sheep and horses on each holding at the latest
quarterly census; for pigs and poultry the basis was a fraction
(in February one-third, reduced in April to one-sixth) of the
numbers returned in 1939. For each type and class of animal,
the nutritional experts calculated an average ration, which
for dairy cows varied with the recorded milk yield. Each
holding thus had a total requirement expressed in terms of
starch and protein, and also certain supplies of home-grown
fodder. It was assumed that the 'maintenance ration' for
each animal—the amount of energy it required just to keep it
alive—would be met from hay, straw, roots and fodder crops;
but the 'productive ration'—the starch and protein required
by dairy cows in giving milk and by other animals in getting
fatter—would be met from cereals, pulse and cattle cake.
The production of cereals and pulse on each holding was
calculated by multiplying its 1939 acreage [1] by the average
county yield, and only if this quantity was less than the
calculated 'production ration' was the occupier entitled to
receive coupons which enabled him to buy from the merchants

---

[1] The acreage returned in 1939 was taken so that farmers who had
ploughed up their grassland and increased their crop production would reap
the benefit.

with whom he registered. ' Surplus ' farmers, whose estimated production of cereals and pulse exceeded the rations allowed, could obtain coupons only if they had sold more than their calculated excess.

In Scotland the Department of Agriculture undertook the task of calculating the theoretical requirements of each holding and its estimated production and also issued the coupons ; in England and Wales the Agricultural Executive Committees were the pivot for the administration. Before rationing was put into force, they had to assemble for each holding the number of livestock, the record of milk sales, the acreage of cereals and pulse and the certificates of quantities sold between harvest and the inception of the scheme. From the prescribed ration scales, the theoretical requirements of each farmer had to be calculated, compared with his production and a balance struck ; the appropriate number of coupons posted to farmers classed as ' deficit ' and a record made for each file. For all this clerical work, staff were required, and the staff required offices, typewriters, chairs and tables. It was not until early in November 1940 that the Committees were optimistically told that a rationing scheme would begin with the new year ; by superhuman efforts, animal rationing did begin in February, and continued to work in spite of pessimistic prophecies to the contrary.

It was indeed unfortunate that this new venture had to be launched in the middle of the farming year rather than in the early autumn at its beginning, for by February most of the wheat and barley had been sold, and the receipts obtained by the farmers were apt to get behind the kitchen clock or mixed up with the sheep dip. Many farmers were thus classed as ' surplus ' when they had in fact sold more than the calculated excess over their requirements, but they could buy no feeds until their appeal had been recorded, substantiated and approved by the over-worked Agricultural Executive Committee. Farmers whose yields were below the county average also found themselves classed as possessors of non-existent grain ; while thousands of small semi-urban holdings had no bulky feeds of their own growing with which to supplement the official rations. And finally there were the holdings which had hitherto escaped all official records, and for which therefore there were neither records nor coupons. In every county the Feedingstuffs Office disappeared under a flood of angry letters followed very shortly by the writers in person ; and the sheer mechanics of handling efficiently such a mass of inquiries and of relating them to the individual farm files involved a degree of organisation to which most committees only attained by slow stages after the initial torrent had subsided. But somehow the officials coped, the coupons went out, the animals were fed and the farmers pacified.

The officials not only surmounted the initial difficulties, but they had introduced a rationing scheme in its most complicated form at the wrong time of the year. From September 1941 the administration was greatly eased by the omission of all calculations about ' surplus ' and ' deficit ' farmers. The supply of rations from the national pool controlled by the Ministry of Food was then restricted to dairy cows, pigs and poultry. The data for the dairy rations were quickly obtained from the monthly invoices of sales through the Milk Marketing Board combined with the quarterly return of livestock ; the rations for pigs and poultry continued to be based on a fraction of the numbers returned in 1939, with some allowance for the size of each holding. In addition, each committee was given a small reserve to be allocated among farmers who, for any approved reason, could neither feed adequately the animals they had nor immediately adjust their livestock to their supplies of fodder. Such appeals led to close investigations on cropping and methods of management which were often much improved by the combined advice of the Feedingstuffs Officer, the Cultivations Officer and the technical experts at their disposal.

The national pool to which these feedingstuffs coupons gave access was fed by two sources derived respectively from millers and merchants. From the flour mills and oilseed-crushing mills, the Ministry of Food obtained a supply of wheat offals and of cattle cake ; from the authorised merchants there was a supply of home-grown oats and barley sold by farmers whose production exceeded their requirements, and who were now legally compelled to sell through recognised channels. When the wheat extraction rate was raised in the spring of 1942, the supply of wheat offals was drastically cut, and the national pool from which the feedingstuff coupons were met depended to a very large extent on the flow of home-grown grain off the farms. And this depended on many factors—the rate of threshing out (which was often interrupted by bad weather), the prospects for autumn grazing or for an early spring, the farmers' estimates of the probable generosity of their committee with its discretionary reserves of cattle cake. If there was a good ' back-end ' to the summer grass, the coupons already issued might lie unused, there would be fewer appeals for supplementary rations and farmers would sell freely their oats and hay. But a dry summer, following perhaps a late spring which had exhausted all reserves of fodder, meant a full off-take of feedingstuff coupons, many appeals for extra help and a reduced rate of sales on the home market. It was not easy therefore for the rationing authorites to adjust effective demand, represented by the coupons it issued, to a level of supplies which varied normally in the opposite direction to the probable requirements ; and at the same time, to accumulate each winter a sufficient reserve to carry oatmeal millers, urban horses and the dairy herds over the summer months after the home crop of grain had all been sold. Because the necessary calculations went on out of the public sight, the public little appreciated the difficulties caused for instance in 1942, when the flour extraction rate was raised, or in the next year when barley was used in flour. The farmers only saw, and grumbled about, the frequent changes in the rationing scale which assumed a steadily rising level of self-sufficiency in feedingstuffs for each holding.

The Harvest of 1941 and Plans for 1942

During the second winter of war, farmers had been asked to plough another $2\frac{1}{4}$ million acres of pasture, and they did in fact convert to crop production just about this amount. The English midlands were no longer an uninterrupted stretch of grass ; on each side wide fields of corn and potatoes revealed the zeal of Agricultural Executive Committees and the patriotism of erstwhile graziers, now converted to arable farmers. Up the west side of the country the plough had bitten deep into neglected dairy pastures, and fields of oats and kale replaced the monthly lorry with its load of compound dairy rations. And this achievement was all the more creditable since the weather was most unfavourable. A wet November put an early stop to the autumn ploughing ; in the new year fierce snow storms and severe frost took a heavy toll of hill sheep and delayed any attempt at field work until well into March. The growth both of crops and the much-needed grass was late, while broken weather at harvesting added to the work and worry of the busiest season of the year. But yields proved eventually to be somewhat above the average ; with nearly 1½ million acres more under corn and another 290,000 acres under potatoes, the food available in the United Kingdom for human consumption in the third year of war showed a marked increase. The production of vegetables had also expanded not only on farms and market gardens but also on allotments where the ' Dig for Victory ' campaign was at its height.

The obverse of this increased crop production was the inevitable decline in animal husbandry, for so long the chief glory of British farmers. There were grave fears over the milk supply. Sales from established herds were steadily falling, and though the Milk Marketing Boards were urging into milk production many cattle-rearing farms in remote districts, total sales continued to fall below the 1939 level, and demand continued to rise. In the winter of 1940–1 the ' manufacturing surplus ' which had so plagued the Boards disappeared ; even when all the milk produced was sold in the liquid market there were shortages in some towns, and consumption kept pace with the increased production in the early summer. Because the Ministry of Food had to provide condensed milk for military use, it imposed restrictions in

A much higher proportion than customary of the total intake of calories would be derived from starchy foods like bread, potatoes and vegetables. Indeed, the rising consumption of potatoes was very marked in the early months of 1941, when the meat ration fell so sharply ; combined with the late arrival of the new potatoes, it created a ten-day gap in supplies in May and June which caused much undeserved blame to descend on the Ministries of Food and Agriculture. But the furore had some useful results ; plans were energetically pushed ahead for a still larger area to be planted with potatoes in 1942, and for acquiring under official control stocks of potatoes, drawn from varieties known to keep well, to fill that uncomfortable gap left by the absence of supplies from the Channel Islands.

In one respect the outlook for food supplies in 1941–2 was immeasurably more hopeful than that for 1940–1. The Lend-Lease Act passed by the United States Congress in March 1941 expelled into the distant future the financial limitations on Britain's ability to buy in a market that still held large stocks of most foods. From the spring of 1941 onwards the Ministry of Food could draw on the resources of trans-Atlantic farms for foods of high nutritional value and little bulk— tinned meats and milk ; dried eggs and desiccated onion ; cheese, fats and bacon. These supplies were indeed welcome. The loss of imports of these foods after June 1940 had pushed the food consumption of the British public down to the lowest level it reached during the Second World War [1] ; with the financial backing of Lend-Lease, supply of animal protein could be gradually improved even though home production inevitably declined. Agricultural production was to be concentrated to an even greater degree on the bulky foods which occupy shipping space.

In 1941–2 farmers in the United Kingdom were asked to find another $1\frac{1}{4}$ million acres of permanent grass for the plough, thus raising the area of arable land to more than 17 million acres by the harvest of 1942. And about $1\frac{1}{4}$ million acres would have to be planted with potatoes, in order to supply

[1] Combined Food Board, *Food Consumption Levels* (H.M.S.O. 1944)

the rising level of consumption even if yields fell to the lowest level of the past decade. The Ministry of Supply was clamouring for flax—more than 150,000 acres of it—to replace the imports no longer available from northern Europe. Another deficiency in supplies, and one which threatened the basis of our agricultural output, was the lack of seeds of many kinds of crops and garden vegetables. To a certain extent substitutes for our normal imports could be drawn from North America, but differences in climate and farming practice limited the usefulness of such untried stocks. To an increasing extent British agriculture had to become self-supporting in seed production ; various scientific institutes, such as the National Institute of Agricultural Botany, the specialist seed-growing firms and the technical experts of the Agricultural Executive Committees, all assisted farmers in the difficult task of growing pure strains of seeds for farms and gardens.

And there was still too little milk, and it seemed there would be even less in the third winter of war. The fall in milk sales was most noticeable in Scotland and in the north-west of England, in such important dairying counties as Cheshire and Lancashire. It was these areas, too, in which milk consumption was increasing most rapidly with rising wages, the absence of unemployment and the shortage of other foods. Before the war the Scottish Milk Marketing Board exported milk to England ; in the winter of 1941-2 Glasgow was drawing milk from England and from Belfast, and the whole pattern of milk transport had to be recast.

The reasons for this falling trend in sales were complex, diverse in their effect on individual farms and not easily analysed at the time. The result reflected the impact of war on the physical and financial resources of more than 150,000 dairy farmers, each confronted with the same problem in a different setting—how to produce milk with a certain amount of land, labour and feedingstuffs. Between the wars the relationship between land and cows was elastic ; with cheap feedingstuffs farmers round the manufacturing towns in Lancashire and the West Riding could keep 40 cows on not many more acres which supplied only summer grazing and a recreation ground. It was these farms which were so drastically affected by the shortages of concentrates on which they depended to an exceptional degree. And northern dairy farmers inevitably used more concentrates in the late autumn and early spring than those in the south-west where grass grew for eight months of the year. Then again the cow bred for high yields could only attain her inherited capacity if she was fed on a diet rich in grain and cattle cake, so that her intake of nutrients was not restricted by her capacity to deal with bulky foods. For such herds the increased consumption of kale and of other fodder crops necessitated by the shortages of concentrates gave the same volume of food but with a lower intake of starch and protein, and milk yields showed the result. It was calculated that average yields per cow had fallen by 10–15 per cent in the first two years of war.

This trend could not quickly be reversed, but its effect on total milk sales could be offset by bringing more farms into the milk business, and by increasing the number of dairy cows on farms which seemed well equipped for them. Winter milk production in particular could be increased by getting more cows to calve in the autumn months and thus levelling down the spring peak in calvings which helped to produce the seasonal peak of milk supplies in May and June. Improvements in management and the culling of the poorest yielders would also help to raise production where output per cow was lowest. In the autumn of 1941 the Agricultural Executive Committees were asked to devote especial attention to those dairy farms in their respective areas whose appeals for supplementary coupons showed them to be in difficulties ; to advise the farmers on breeding policy and the management of home-grown fodder ; to give them priority in the supply of Land Girls, fertilisers and tractors for their crop production. An appeal for more winter milk was sent to every dairy farmer ; a Victory Churn Contest was launched on a wave of official speeches to be won by the counties collectively and farmers individually who managed to show the greatest increase in milk production in 1942–3.

After Pearl Harbour

The bombs which fell on Pearl Harbour on 6 December 1941 convinced Mr Churchill that the Allies had won the war. ' Many disasters, immeasurable cost and tribulation lay ahead, but there was no more doubt about the end.' [1] For British agriculture the immediate result of ' global war ' was a call for an intensification of its effort. Shipping had been the weakest link in Britain's effort in 1941, but in 1942 it nearly snapped under the double strain of the Pacific war and the attack by German submarines on unprotected vessels in the western Atlantic. For the greater part of 1942 losses of ships exceeded the gains from new construction ; and when the balance was reversed at the end of the year armies and their equipment were awaiting transport to North Africa, to Burma, to Sicily and Italy. [2]

To reduce still further the claims of the civilian economy to shipping, farmers in the United Kingdom would be called upon to sow a still greater acreage with bread grains for the harvest of 1943 ; but immediately, in the year of 1942, further economy in shipping meant using for human consumption a higher proportion of the cereals grown in 1941. It meant the raising in April 1942 of the wheat extraction rate to 85 per cent, giving to consumers a loaf that was definitely grey and to farmers still smaller rations of feedingstuffs. And, too, it was agreed that wheat imports in 1943 must be cut by using dried potatoes in bread, or, failing potatoes, oats, rye and barley which would have to be withdrawn from the feeding-stuffs pool after the 1942 harvest. From November barley ranked legally with wheat and rye as a crop which had to be sold to an approved buyer, and which could not be used for animals.

---

[1] Churchill, W. S., *The Second World War*, vol. iii, ' The Grand Alliance,' p. 539, 540 (Cassell 1950)
[2] Hancock, W. K. and Gowing, M. M., op. cit., p. 414, and for the relationship in 1942-4 of ships and U.K. food stocks, see pp. 419-35

The loss of wheat offals was a serious matter, more serious than might be expected from the quantitative fall in tonnage. For dietetic reasons wheat offals were a valuable food for young pigs after weaning and for young chickens, and could not satisfactorily be replaced by any substitute. Two conclusions followed : firstly, a further cut in the allowances to farm pigs and poultry to supply only one-eighth (instead of one-sixth) of pre-war numbers ; and secondly, some check to the growing population of pigs and poultry kept in back yards and gardens. British citizens had indeed been officially encouraged to keep pigs, rabbits and poultry on the theory that kitchen and garden waste, supplemented by a limited ration of meal, could thus be usefully converted into food. But the right of any citizen to buy such rations for his domestic stock led to a rapid multiplication in their numbers which now threatened to absorb the cereals required to supply the commercial holdings from which alone the Ministry of Food drew supplies of eggs and bacon pigs for distribution to urban consumers. From July 1942 the authorities limited the issue of domestic ' balancer meal ' to the supply of one hen for each shell egg coupon surrendered from the ration book, thus ensuring that the domestic poultry keeper did not also buy eggs from a shop ; and from September rations were halved for pigs kept by pig clubs and persons other than farmers. As was expected, the number of breeding sows and of young pigs showed a renewed fall in the winter of 1942–3. There was no further use for those pre-war toys, the fattening houses with central heating and trolley ways for feeding pigs on standard rations of wheatings. The farmyard sow reverted to the habits of the pre-scientific age ; she lived on swill, tail corn, chat potatoes, mangolds and grass, and brought up her litter to accept the same diet, with only occasional help from the meal merchant.

One immediate effect of the extension of the war was thus to intensify the scarcity of cereals in Britain, and also the need for their greater production. Two further results may also be noted which were slower to develop. One has already been briefly mentioned, the check given to the mechanisation

CHAPTER VII

PRODUCTION AT THE PEAK, 1942-4

SINGAPORE fell to the Japanese armies after Britain's two battleships, the *Prince of Wales* and the *Repulse*, had been sunk by air attack ; Burma, Java and the Philippines were overrun. For the second time the British forces were driven out of North Africa back into Egypt, while the German armies continued to push eastward into Russia. The first half of 1942 was not a cheerful time for the Allies, but at least British farmers could watch with pride and anxiety their ripening harvest through the long days of a dry summer. In spite of patchy weather at harvesting, yields were remarkably high ; an average yield of more than a ton was recorded for the $2\frac{1}{2}$ million acres of wheat, and of more than 7 tons for potatoes. Three winters of severe frosts and three dry springs had brought into good condition the heavy clay soils which, producing indifferent grass before the war, contributed magnificent grain crops in 1942. Farmers grew more than the targets set for potatoes and sugar-beet, and they very nearly attained the allotted area for that highly unpopular crop, flax. The harvesting of some 7 million tons of grain from $8\frac{1}{2}$ million acres implied a gigantic effort by men and their machines. More than a thousand combines were engaged in the work ; they undoubtedly saved labour on the farm, but their use involved the merchants and millers in acute problems over bagging, transport and drying of grain, which was marketed straight from the fields. (The Ministry of Food found itself committed to the building of silos and grain dryers as the flow of combines continued.) Binders had also been imported in quantity, but were suddenly threatened with extinction because binder twine was made from hemp, and hemp no longer came from the Philippines. By mobilising all stocks enough was found to supply the 1942 harvest, leaving to later years the development of substitutes.

The high yields and extended area of the 1942 harvest undoubtedly eased the shipping shortage of the first year of global war; in 1942 and 1943 the British civilian fed slightly better than in the leanest months of 1941, and with a considerably lower level of food imports. It was a monotonous diet, with a rising consumption of 'fillers' such as bread, potatoes and vegetables to counterbalance the smaller supplies of meat, fats, eggs, fruit and sugar. The non-priority consumer was cut to two pints of fresh milk per week in the winter, and the arrival of the monthly egg-in-shell was a red-letter day in October, November and December. Apart from the home-grown foods, the diet was increasingly derived from dried products packed in tins on the other side of the Atlantic—spam and dried egg and powdered skimmed milk and corned beef; the diet was indeed monotonous but it sufficed.

PLANNING THE HARVESTS

The interval which elapses between devising a plan for agriculture and its realisation is apt to confuse alike the plans and their historian. In the spring of 1942, within a few weeks of Pearl Harbour, administrators began to programme for the harvest of 1943, which was to be planted in the winter of 1942–3 and which would feed the British nation in 1943–4, two years ahead. The plans had to be announced to farmers in July or August 1942, before the ploughs began to turn the furrows for autumn-sown wheat; thereafter, only minor modifications could be made to take effect with the spring sowing of barley, oats and potatoes.

The plans for this harvest were inevitably part of the strategy of war, in which the technicalities of farming had their place. The problem was to synchronise the year of greatest output from agriculture with the year of greatest stringency in shipping, which depended primarily on the date to be fixed for the invasion of Europe by the Allied armies and on the duration of the subsequent and final battles. In the spring of 1942 this decision had not been made, but it lay between 1943 and 1944, with a strong bias in favour of the

earlier year. And so the agricultural planners chose the 1943
harvest (to be consumed in 1943–4) as the year of peak production from British farms.

Let us consider for a moment the technical factors involved
in such a plan. No one crop can be grown on the same
land for more than a few years in succession without risking
a considerable fall in yields. Modern science and modern
fertilisers may have lengthened the interval during which
one crop can be continuously cultivated, but infestation by
weeds, pests and diseases eventually becomes acute and yields
suffer. (It was this age-old experience which led to the
medieval rotation of winter corn, spring corn and fallow ;
and to the adoption in the nineteenth century of the Norfolk
four-course rotation of corn, roots, corn and clover.) By
1942 much of the land broken from grass since 1939 would
have carried two or even three crops of grain or potatoes in
succession ; many farmers on old arable took corn after
corn in 1941 and 1942 in response to the call for bread grains
and for winter feed for their dairy herds. The process might
be repeated once, perhaps even twice, if the need were desperate, though agricultural opinion was strongly against it.
By 1944, or 1945 at the latest, the proportion of arable land
under corn and potatoes would have to be reduced, and that
under restorative crops, roots and grass, be allowed to increase.

This trend would indeed be mitigated if fresh land could
be found for the plough, if still more grassland could be
turned into arable, as arable went down to temporary grass.
But the United Kingdom had already lost five million acres
of grassland ; what remained was that least suitable for cultivation. If the area under crops was to be increased in 1943
and possibly maintained in 1944, the plough would have to go
farther up the hills where the slopes were steeper and the soil
thinner ; farther into the bracken and furze which mark the
patches of sand and gravel ; and farther into those inaccessible
and waterlogged clay fields which would have first to be
drained. Such land would demand a great effort to bring
it into cultivation ; it would generally be inherently less
productive than that already under crop ; it would generally

be more deficient at the start in all the basic requirements—drainage, lime, phosphates, roads and fences and water for livestock.

In the summer of 1942 it was thought that some half-million such acres could be found for the plough in the forthcoming season, and an equivalent area was to be added to the already large production of wheat, potatoes and vegetables. But the decision taken in October 1942 to add rye, barley or oats to the loaf in order to supplement the supply of bread grain led to a revision of the cropping programmes. The Agricultural Executive Committees were finally asked to obtain at least a million acres of old grassland for the plough ; and a similar addition to the area under grain, with special emphasis on spring-sown wheat and barley, which were more suitable than oats for inclusion in the ' national flour.' The area under potatoes, sugar-beet and flax would have to be maintained at not less than that of the previous year ; for these crops and for wheat, the Committees were, if necessary, to issue compulsory directions on farmers with suitable land. And as far as possible these further acreages of crops for human consumption were not to diminish the supply of high-quality feeds for dairy herds ; the improvement in milk sales shown for the first time in the summer of 1942 was to be encouraged in every way.

The prospect for 1943 of some $18\frac{1}{2}$ million acres of crops and temporary grass, compared with the 1939 total of nearly 13 million acres, must have made the Agricultural Departments acutely conscious of two basic theorems of economics—the law of diminishing returns, and the need to allocate scarce resources between the satisfaction of different wants. For much of the land brought into cultivation at this stage of the war was ' marginal ' in the economic sense ; the yields from it were likely to be low, the costs of breaking it in and cultivating it were likely to be high, leading to a high cost per ton of grain or potatoes. But that crop of grain or potatoes was required ; some method had to be found of financing this high-cost production, of inducing farmers to grow crops which in a normal world would be ' uneconomic.' The problem of financing marginal production was closely connected with the general changes in wages and in prices which had occurred during the war and is discussed with them in the next chapter.

LIMITING FACTORS

The allocation of scarce resources among different purposes was the most important factor in 1942-3, dominating the whole strategy of economic effort as well as that section represented by agriculture. The principal shortages foreseen for farming for 1942-3 were in machinery, in fertilisers and lime, and finally, the most important of all, in manpower. Let us look briefly at each of these limiting factors.

(a) Machinery

For machinery the problem was to secure the best distribution of supplies which, though large in relation to the pre-war output, had become inadequate to meet an increased demand and which were likely to fall in the near future. The only answer was a rigorous selection in priorities, both in supply, to ensure that only the most urgently needed types were manufactured or imported, and in demand, to ensure that each tractor or combine went where it would add most to output. The first was achieved through the centralised control exercised by the Government over imports, and through the developing co-operation between the Agricultural Departments and the home manufacturers of tractors and implements. The rationing of demand was entrusted in 1942 to the Agricultural Executive Committees, with their now detailed knowledge of the cropping programme for each farm in their respective areas. For every year or half-year the probable supply of the major items was allocated among the Committees, taking into account the existing machinery in their area and the planned crop acreage ; from the scores of approved applications on its files (including probably one from its own Machinery Contracts Service), each Committee had then to allot its quota by some order of urgency, or nuisance-value. In addition, many Committees organised instruction courses in machinery maintenance and operation for the benefit of new owners ; and they encouraged the formation of local groups of farmers who jointly acquired some expensive item for their mutual benefit.

(b) Fertilisers and Lime

The extended cropping programme for 1943 greatly intensified the existing shortage of some types of fertilisers, caused principally by the rapid increase in demand. Profitable prices, the preaching of the Agricultural Executive Committees and the increasing crop acreage had all combined to make farmers more ' fertiliser-conscious.' The supply of nitrogenous fertilisers had expanded to keep pace with demand in the early years of war ; even in 1943 and later seasons, the occasional deficiencies in supply were caused more by difficulties in transport than by a failure in production. But supplies of potash were derived from imports. Before the war, potash came from Germany and Alsace, and after 1940 the available supply in this country was almost halved until fresh sources were tapped. That shortage was a serious matter, for potatoes, sugar-beet, vegetables and flax, all crops whose production was greatly expanded in war, required comparatively heavy applications of potassic fertilisers. From the autumn of 1940 the use of potash was legally restricted to these crops, and to land certified by the Agricultural Executive Committes to be seriously lacking in this element. But by 1943 suspected potash deficiency was reported from a number of areas as a cause, principal or contributory, of crop failures, and it was fortunate that a steady improvement in supplies was secured from 1944 onwards.

The scarcity of phosphates was not, at first, as acute as that of potash. The supply of basic slag increased rapidly with the rising output of steel in the early years of war ; and although imports of phosphate rock from North Africa were interrupted after 1940, alternative sources were developed from islands in the Pacific, at the expense of a much longer voyage. But the war with Japan temporarily stopped this development, and imports of phosphatic fertilisers from the United States could barely fill the deficiency. And this inelasticity of supply was a serious handicap for increasing agricultural output. Soil experts were well aware that the general use of phosphates was far less than it should be ; few farmers realised how deficient old grassland usually was in phosphates and lime, and the dressings normally given to the new arable were seldom adequate to ensure a strong crop and reasonable yield. And the ploughing campaign planned for 1943 would involve another million acres of ' marginal grassland,' for which supplies both of phosphates and lime must be found, even at the risk of cutting short the crops grown on old arable. There had been in 1941 complaints that farmers could not get the phosphates they were directed to apply, and in 1942-3 phosphates were put on the ration together with potash. The probable supplies for the season were divided among Executive Committees in proportion to the arable in their districts, with an extra allowance for those areas known to be exceptionally deficient ; Committees were told that they could follow the same principle in allocating their quota among their farmers, or, if they had the staff, they could base their farm rations on actual soil samples.

It was one of the ironies of war that so many farmers first learnt the value of fertilisers at a time when supplies were strictly limited by loss of overseas sources and by the shortage of ships. It was inevitable that rationing should operate chiefly to restrict the purchase of fertilisers by those farmers who habitually bought fair amounts in order to supply those whose land had been seriously neglected before the war, a result that naturally caused ill-feeling. But for lime, entirely home produced, there was a brighter prospect. There had indeed been some falling off in production in the first year of war, but this served to stimulate official action. Lime quarries were given a high priority in supplies of labour and of fuel ; new crushing plants were imported from America in order to develop new sources or to re-open old workings ; transport congestion was minimised by careful planning of distribution and by special rebates to farmers who would take delivery in the summer. By these means the pre-war output was doubled in 1942-3, and the expansion continued in sub-

sequent years though at a slower rate ; complaints, mainly
from Scotland, about scarcity were due more often to difficulties in the transport and delivery of so bulky a product
than to deficiency in production.

(c) Manpower

Behind all these problems of scarcity and rationing lay
the greatest scarcity of all—that of labour. Quite early in
1941 the attempt begun in the previous June to find 100,000
men for agricultural work had been tacitly dropped ; by the
autumn of that year there were no unemployed men anywhere
in the country, yet the demand for manpower continued to
expand. The mechanism of the Essential Works Order was
then applied to the Agricultural Executive Committees ; in
return for a guaranteed weekly wage, employees could neither
leave, nor be dismissed by, the Committees without the permission of the local office of the Ministry of Labour. In
Scotland, where the tradition of the half-yearly ' flitting ' was
strong, a further step was taken ; it became illegal for any male
worker to change his job without such permission. A regulation of that type threw a heavy load of work on to the Ministry
of Labour, and it was never applied south of the Border.
However, exemption from military service was only granted
to men judged to be indispensable in their work at the time
of their registration, and this proved a considerable check on
unnecessary moves from one farm to another within agriculture itself.

These measures could only serve to improve the use made
of the existing manpower ; an increase in the total supply
devoted to war production could only be obtained by calling
on the women previously employed at home or in less essential
industries. In December 1941 the Government broke with
tradition by introducing compulsory national service for
women between 20 and 30 years, and the age groups were
gradually extended to include finally both the $18\frac{1}{2}$-year-olds
and women not exceeding 50. During 1942 there was a rapid
expansion in the Women's Land Army both from volunteers
and from women registering under the National Service Acts ;

on such women, farmers depended for the extra work involved in the dairy and in the fields by the production programme for the harvest of 1943 :

NUMBER OF WORKERS ON AGRICULTURAL HOLDINGS [1]

	U.K.			
	Regular			Casual
	Men	Women	Total	
	1000's	1000's	1000's	1000's
June 1939	592	71	663	140
1940	578	78	656	150
1941	578	89	667	183
1942	578	130	708	207
1943	567	157	724	232
1944	572	173*	745*	205

* Including 48,000 W.L.A. in England and Wales separately recorded for the first time, but excluding 25,000 prisoners of war.

Even this expansion failed to keep pace with the increasing demand for Land Girls from farmers and Executive Committees in all parts of Britain, but efforts to increase the rate of recruitment over the winter of 1942–3 brought little response. By the early months of 1943 the country was found to be fully mobilised for war, with about half its total labour force engaged either in the armed services, in civil defence or in civilian war employment. All that remained was to change the distribution of manpower as the strategy of war demanded, and in 1943 and 1944 that strategy demanded the concentration of manpower on transport, aircraft and military construction. As the crops ripened through the long days of a glorious summer, it was realised that there could be little further expansion in the agricultural labour force, apart from such prisoners as the fortunes of war might make available. Recruitment to the

[1] *Agricultural Statistics U.K., 1939–44*, Part i (H.M.S.O. 1948)

Land Army was restricted from July 1943 to the numbers required to maintain the existing strength, which was generally admitted to be inadequate to the volume of work.

It was therefore indeed fortunate that the weather was for once on the side of the harvesters. Another spring drought—a curiously persistent feature of the war years—delayed both crops and grass, but moderate and seasonable rains were quickly followed by a long spell of sunshine. The early harvest was of great asistance in spreading the peak intensity of work for men and machines, and in southern and eastern districts corn, potatoes and beet were all gathered in good condition, though pastures were bare and the hay crop light. But in western and northern districts the weather broke in August ; sheaves stooked then were in some places still standing out in October, and the potato lifting was a nightmare of waterlogged fields and constant rain. Grass, oats and fodder crops these farmers could grow, but the large area of wheat and barley for which the Government had asked was too big a risk in the face of the vagaries of the weather.

THE HARVEST OF 1944

There was no hope after 1943 that the number of workers could be appreciably enlarged ; there were acute scarcities of potash, phosphates, harvesting machinery, binder twine, sacks and a hundred other necessities ranging from milk churns and fencing wire to Dutch barns and crawler tractors. Both farmers and technical experts pressed for some relaxation of cropping, and emphasised the risks of planting larger acreages than could reasonably be cultivated and harvested. For whatever the planned area, it all had to be gathered in those same few weeks in the late summer and autumn. Already the corn harvest overlapped with the lifting of potatoes ; and the sugar-beet and the roots had to be left until the 9 million tons of potatoes had been bagged for immediate sale or stored in clamps. And there was the spread of potato eelworm in the districts of intensive production and the highest yields, for which pest only one cure was known—not to grow potatoes.

The returns for June 1943, when they became available, revealed one significant trend. Nearly $1\frac{1}{4}$ million acres of grassland had been ploughed up and added to the total arable area, but the area under crops and bare fallow had only risen by 900,000 acres. For the area of temporary grass (which had reached a minimum in 1941) now exceeded the pre-war level, a pointer to the fact that corn production was at its peak. Farmers had added more than a million acres to the 1942 production of wheat and barley, but at the expense of 450,000 acres of oats, the principal fodder grain. This was a grave danger to the volume of milk sales, whose downward trend had been halted in 1942 and reversed in the first half of 1943. It looked as though the production of bread grain on the 1943 scale could only be continued at the expense of milk production.

The weight of agricultural opinion was probably against the final decision to maintain for 1944 the 1943 area of bread grains and potatoes ; the resources available seemed inadequate to sustain so vast an effort for another twelve months. But wars are not won without taking some risks ; and this policy for food production was determined by a still greater risk—a possible shortage of ships to mount the invasion of Europe which it was now realised could not be executed before the summer of 1944. The duration of that final battle could not be foreseen, but it was only reasonable to assume that a substantial part of Europe would require to be fed from the Allied harvest of 1944.

Briefly, the plan for 1944 was to hold what had been obtained in 1943. The areas to be planted with wheat, barley, potatoes and sugar-beet were not to be diminished. But since some of the arable needed a rest in temporary grass, it was hoped to bring into crop production an equivalent area from the greatly diminished pasture. Such a trend would, it was expected, increase the amount of grass available, since new leys, properly treated, should be far more productive than the ' marginal ' land which was now all that remained to be ploughed. And one relaxation in austerity was granted. The dilution of bread with barley and of beer with oats was suspended in the autumn of 1943, thus releasing for the feeding-stuff ration a useful amount of the latter crop. Better grass and more oats were to maintain milk production and to provide slightly larger rations for pigs and poultry, which encouraged the rebuilding of the breeding stocks to supply a post-war world at last within sight.

But though the Government might plan to maintain production in 1944, it could not plan the weather for that year. Yet another spell of hot dry weather in spring and summer raised hopes for another great harvest, but in August the weather broke all over the country. The harvesting of these $9\frac{1}{2}$ million acres of corn and $1\frac{1}{4}$ million acres of potatoes and beet was a continuous struggle against gales, rain and winter, while in south-eastern England flying bombs added a grim element of danger. There were fair yields of wheat and barley, but those for oats, potatoes and beet were rather below normal ; the final result was a small decline in total output from that achieved in the more favourable conditions of 1943.

The Achievement

It may be well to pause at this point and to assess what British agriculture had in fact achieved, and to consider the structural changes which had occurred within it. The financial changes are described in the next chapter, but here we may look briefly at the estimates of total production and at the varied experiences of the different types of farming.

There is no single measure of the changes in output which is satisfactory for all purposes—for judging the increased effort demanded of farmers and their workers, their contribution to the national diet, or the shipping they saved.[1] Farmers produced more of most things by producing less of some ; we cannot without careful qualification compare an output

[1] On this point, see *How Britain was Fed in War Time* (H.M.S.O. 1946) ; *Agricultural Statistics, 1939-44 U.K.*, Part ii, p. 12–30 ; J. H. Kirk, The 'Output of British Agriculture during the War,' *Journal, Agricultural Economics Society*, December 1945

of 1 million tons of wheat and 1 million tons of pig meat with another consisting of 1½ million tons of wheat and a ½ million tons of pig meat, and say that the latter is ' greater ' than the former. The sale in 1943–4 of slightly more milk than in pre-war years is no measure of the agricultural effort involved, unless we take into account the degree to which farmers replaced imported feedingstuffs by greatly increased supplies of home-grown fodder, at the same time as they grew larger acreages of crops for human consumption.

We can begin with the most obvious measure of output, that of money value. The gross output (defined as commodities sold off agricultural holdings in the United Kingdom for use of the non-farming population) increased from £285 millions in the average of the three pre-war years to a little under £600 millions in 1943–4. If we deduct from these figures the value of the raw materials which agriculture bought (imported seeds, feedingstuffs and animals), there remains a value for net output which rose from £195 millions to £535 millions. But a substantial part of this rise is clearly due to changes in price. To obtain a more accurate measure of changes in quantity, the annual net output has been re-valued at constant prices and the result expressed as a percentage of the pre-war years. On this basis agricultural net output rose to 111 per cent in 1940–1, and, after a slight decline, to 125 per cent of the pre-war level in 1942–3, and to 128 per cent in 1943–4, the highest point reached during the war.

Another, but less definite, measure of the expansion in home production is given by the decline in imports of food and feedingstuffs, from 23 million tons in 1938 to just 11 million tons in 1944. Of this economy in shipping space (a vital factor in the early years of war), about half was due to the absence of imported feedingstuffs, for which British agriculture grew substitutes ; the greater output of bread grains was another factor, together with changes in the national diet, symbolised by food rationing, by ' national wholemeal bread,' and the absence of much of the variety and palatability which characterised the pre-war diet of all except the poorest.

This concentration of home production on the bulky crops for direct human consumption meant that some 40 per cent of the total intake of calories was home-grown in 1944 compared with some 30 per cent in the pre-war years.

For the agricultural community itself the most striking measure of its war-time output was the reversal of the pre-war proportions of arable and grassland :

USE OF AGRICULTURAL LAND IN THE UNITED KINGDOM

	1939	1943	1944
	Million Acres		
Tillage	8·8	14·5	14·6
Temporary Grass	4·1	4·2	4·7
Total Arable Land	12·9	18·7	19·3
Permanent Grass	18·8	12·4	11·7
Total Crops and Grass	31·7	31·1	31·0

The loss of agricultural land during these years, lost under aerodromes, camps and battle-training areas, exceeded the total brought back to agricultural use by more than 700,000 acres ; on a somewhat smaller total area farmers had in 1944 half a million more acres of arable land than they had permanent grass in 1939.

The production of crops on this scale implied a gigantic effort by farmers and their men. Nearly $9\frac{1}{2}$ million acres of corn had to be sown in the same few weeks of autumn or early spring that had sufficed for the $5\frac{1}{4}$ million acres of 1939 ; nearly $9\frac{1}{2}$ million acres of corn and $1\frac{1}{2}$ million acres of potatoes and sugar-beet had to be harvested in those treacherous weeks between mid-July and the onset of the winter frosts. It was this intensified seasonal pressure of work which weighed so heavily on the farmers and their staff, and which forced on agriculture the use of casual labour on a vast scale. The sheep, pigs and poultry which had practically disappeared from many lowland farms had required attendance on a scale which did not greatly vary from one month to another ; the new crops which replaced the livestock demanded not only a general increase in field work for most of the year, but a huge increase in man-hours at the peaks of spring sowing, potato planting, the corn harvest and the potato lifting. To an increasing extent the production of corn was mechanised —the combine harvesters alone greatly helped to relieve the pressure in the autumn, but it was the potato crop in particular which added to the farmers' burdens in these years.

The Ministry of Food regarded the unrationed supply of potatoes as a war-time essential ; it insisted on an acreage that would supply the increasing demand even at the lowest yields recently experienced ; it pointed, in justification for its action, at the high yield of calories obtained from an acre of potatoes. These arguments proved decisive, and farmers did in fact plant every year a slightly larger acreage of potatoes than was set. But as a method of providing calories, potato production was perhaps less successful than the nutritionists realised. For although an acre of potatoes contains more calories than an acre of wheat, in most of the war years three-quarters of the wheat grown was finally eaten by humans ; potatoes had a far higher rate of wastage, amounting in years of blight or of high yields to nearly half the crop. Thus in 1943–4, of 3·4 million tons of wheat, 2·8 million tons was sold off farms for human consumption, but only 6 out of the 9·8 million tons of potatoes. Yet nearly 10 million tons of potatoes had to be lifted in the autumn of 1943, and either bagged for immediate sale, or clamped for storage, to be at some later date dug out, sorted and then bagged, all by hand.

For all this extra work farmers had slightly fewer experienced men, considerably more women and a much larger number of casual workers than before the war. The casual workers included school children, recruited mainly for potato planting and lifting, and who therefore did not feature in the statistics collected in June of each year ; townsfolk on holiday living in camps organised by the Agricultural Executive Committees ; local residents who gave a hand as their other duties allowed ; prisoners of war ; and the organised gangs of the Land Army who were directly employed by the Agricultural Executive Committees, and worked for those farmers judged by the Labour Officer to be in greatest need. Without the assistance of these thousands the war-time harvests could never have been gathered ; but, equally, as long as farmers could be reasonably sure of obtaining a gang of workers at any time by telephoning the Labour Officer, there was no inducement for them to improve their management of labour against the day when the Land Army was demobilised and the prisoners went home.

THE CHANGE IN FARMING SYSTEMS

These deductions from the national statistics provide generalisations which have only limited validity when applied to the many types of farming to be found in these islands. The impact of war was felt very differently in Leicestershire and in Lincolnshire, in Midlothian and in Merioneth ; the technical and economic changes varied in magnitude and kind from one county to another and often from one farm to another.

The features of soil, climate and topography which largely determine our types of farming have little relation to county boundaries, but if minor variations in farming systems are ignored, it is possible to illustrate from the county statistics some of the more striking changes brought about between 1939 and 1944. The following tables bring together the acreage and livestock figures for seven groups of counties, each group comprising between 500,000 and 1 million acres of crops and grass. The statistics for 1949 have been added to bring the comparison up to the end of the decade.

Take first the eastern arable region which had before the war four-fifths of its area under crops, mainly wheat and barley, potatoes, sugar-beet and vegetables. This was already a region of cash crops which in the nineteen-thirties farmed the wheat act and the sugar-beet subsidy, and whose livestock were largely kept to turn into muck the by-products of the crops. War brought little change to these arable farmers who ploughed the outlying pastures, sold a higher proportion of their corn crops and gradually disposed of their pigs and sheep. Gradually, too, they added to their equipment the new or improved types of machinery—a combine harvester or a potato lifter. This was, however, already a well-mechanised region with a village population already accustomed to give a hand with pea picking or potato lifting.

The Scottish arable farmers worked more strictly on a rotation with two or more years in grass which grew better than in the drier and hotter south. For them the war meant the ploughing up not only of the pastures lying on the foothills but also of their leys. The proportion under temporary grass shrank from one-third of the arable to one quarter, as an extra crop of oats or barley was taken instead of a second year's grazing ; the substantial increase in potato production (mainly to supply seed to the English markets) created a substantial demand for seasonal labour which was met by Land Girls and school children. The lack of purchased feeds made it difficult to maintain milk yields in this district of late springs and housed dairies ; yet the general shortage of milk in Scotland and the favourable prices for it brought a steady increase in the numbers of milk cows, while those of sheep fell by about one-quarter. A shortening of the ley and an intensified output of cash crops marked this district in which there was a seasonal but not general shortage of labour.

In contrast to these two arable regions, compare the record for the midland grazing counties of Leicester, Rutland and Warwick. In 1939 there were patches of market gardens in favourable localities and occasional fields of corn or roots which amounted to less than one-fifth of the total area. Permanent pastures covered four-fifths of these million acres, and they were grazed by dairy cows supplying the midland towns, by fattening cattle and by more than 600,000 sheep, often bought in each year for a few months grazing on their way from the hills to the butchers.

To this type of farming war meant revolution, to be effected with machinery that had still to be acquired, with men who had

TABLE I

	Corn	Man-golds Turnips and Swedes	Potatoes and Sugar-beet	Total Tillage	Temp. Grass	Total Arable
			1000 acres			

I   EASTERN ARABLE (Cambs., Isle of Ely, Holland)

	Corn	Mangolds etc.	Potatoes etc.	Total Tillage	Temp. Grass	Total Arable
1939	266·4	13·6	153·1	520·0	38·6	558·7
1944	301·5	12·0	172·2	574·4	48·6	609·5
1949	287·4	11·0	157·8	577·4	57·6	625·0
% of 1939	108	81	103	111	149	112

II   SCOTTISH ARABLE (Angus, East Lothian, Midlothian, Fife)

1939	192·0	55·5	55·1	318·0	186·3	504·4
1944	257·1	56·4	85·2	422·3	151·1	573·4
1949	218·1	53·9	69·1	363·8	184·4	548·2
% of 1939	114	98	125	114	99	109

III   MIDLAND GRAZING (Leicester, Rutland, Warwick)

1939	95·5	14·2	9·4	148·0	41·1	189·0
1944	347·8	23·5	41·4	460·5	113·4	573·9
1949	278·6	19·0	35·7	384·8	159·9	544·7
% of 1939	292	134	380	260	389	289

IV   DAIRY FARMING (Cheshire, Stafford)

1939	108·4	15·6	31·0	171·5	92·9	264·3
1944	237·4	32·1	54·1	346·4	136·6	483·0
1949	202·5	21·6	50·1	296·3	159·1	455·4
% of 1939	187	138	162	173	171	172

V   SOUTH-WEST MIXED (Devon)

1939	135·2	37·3	6·8	221·6	193·8	415·4
1944	301·0	46·8	32·7	443·9	152·5	596·4
1949	215·6	37·3	25·9	336·3	210·7	547·0
% of 1939	160	100	381	152	109	132

VI   NORTHERN HILL FARMING (Durham, Northumberland)

1939	109·2	29·6	17·9	167·8	93·8	261·6
1944	294·4	43·7	39·1	405·0	133·5	538·6
1949	219·9	35·7	35·1	312·7	166·5	479·2
% of 1939	201	121	196	186	178	183

VII   WELSH HILL FARMING (Brecon, Cardigan, Merioneth, Radnor)

1939	67·7	11·7	4·3	90·3	75·2	165·4
1944	131·8	16·8	14·4	202·5	108·9	311·4
1949	107·1	13·6	12·2	158·7	120·2	278·9
% of 1939	158	116	284	176	160	169

Percentage of Arable in				Perm. Grass	Total Crops and Grass	% of Crops and Grass in	
Corn	Fodder Roots	Potatoes and Beet	Temp. Grass			Arable	Perm. Grass
1000 acres							
48	2½	27½	7	147·3	705·9	79	21
49½	2	28½	8	100·3	709·7	86	14
46	1½	25	9	86·8	711·8	88	12
—	—	—	—	59	101	—	—
38	11	11	37	186·5	690·8	83	17
45	10	15	26	106·3	679·6	84	16
40	10	12½	34	130·1	678·3	80	20
—	—	—	—	70	98	—	—
50½	7½	5	21½	807·0	996·0	19	81
60½	4	7	20	416·0	989·9	58	42
51	3½	6½	29	444·9	989·6	55	45
—	—	—	—	55	99	—	—
41	6	12	35	752·7	1017·1	26	74
49	6½	11	28	527·1	1010·1	48	52
44½	5	11	35	546·4	1001·8	45½	54½
—	—	—	—	73	99	—	—
32½	9	1½	47	708·3	1123·7	37	63
50	8	5½	25½	526·1	1122·5	53	47
39½	7	5	38½	588·9	1135·9	48	52
—	—	—	—	83	101	—	—
42	11	7	36	757·0	1018·6	26	74
55	8	7	25	432·0	970·6	55½	44½
46	7	7	35	481·9	961·1	50	50
—	—	—	—	64	94	—	—
41	7	2½	45½	513·8	679·2	24½	75½
42	5½	4½	35	314·8	626·2	50	50
38½	5	4½	43	345·0	623·9	45	55
—	—	—	—	67	92	—	—

TABLE II LIVESTOCK,

	Cows or Heifers	Other Cattle over 2 years	Total Cattle
	1000's	1000's	1000's
I EASTERN ARABLE (Cambs., Isle of Ely, Holland)			
1939	24·9	13·8	74·9
1944	28·5	19·1	81·6
1949	26·0	19·5	80·4
% of 1939	104	141	107
II SCOTTISH ARABLE (Angus, East Lothian, Midlothian, Fife)			
1939	41·3	41·2	144·7
1944	46·3	41·7	143·7
1949	56·1	43·4	169·9
% of 1939	136	105	117
III MIDLAND GRAZING (Leicester, Rutland, Warwick)			
1939	123·4	79·9	325·2
1944	134·1	58·4	305·5
1949	139·1	69·5	335·7
% of 1939	113	87	103
IV DAIRY FARMING (Cheshire, Stafford)			
1939	290·4	26·5	455·1
1944	309·0	27·0	472·8
1949	306·3	31·9	485·9
% of 1939	106	120	107
V SOUTH-WEST MIXED (Devon)			
1939	134·1	39·3	339·4
1944	158·9	48·4	375·5
1949	169·6	57·0	414·0
% of 1939	126½	145	122
VI NORTHERN HILL FARMING (Durham, Northumberland)			
1939	84·8	97·5	294·8
1944	94·0	88·0	284·8
1949	98·4	107·3	322·4
% of 1939	116	110	109
VII WELSH HILL FARMING (Brecon, Cardigan, Merioneth, Radnor)			
1939	69·4	18·2	178·2
1944	83·5	24·8	197·7
1949	90·6	23·5	207·7
% of 1939	131	129	117

(a) May 1942

Sheep	Pigs	Workers		Tractors
		Regular	Casual	
1000's	1000's	1000's	1000's	
70·1	169·7	28·0	9·2	4,882(a)
41·8	56·8	28·9	10·2	6,371
28·2	96·2	29·1	10·4	12,985(b)
40	57	104	112	—
740·6	58·4	16·4	3·1	2,500(a)
514·6	48·2	17·9	4·3	3,653
561·8	71·0	17·1	3·2	6,332(b)
76	122	104	102	—
631·9	84·2	14·0	2·2	4,867(a)
255·6	46·7	19·7	4·7	7,003
251·6	69·7	19·0	4·9	11,927(b)
40	83	136	223	—
332·5	174·3	23·3	3·8	3,460(a)
130·1	54·2	25·8	6·8	5,156
122·8	94·8	26·7	6·8	11,305(b)
37	54	115	179	—
973·2	156·8	16·6	3·9	3,053(a)
805·1	54·8	18·6	5·3	6,036
739·7	68·8	19·4	4·9	12,173(b)
76	44	116½	126	—
1445·3	48·1	14·3	2·4	3,285(a)
1099·0	35·1	18·9	4·4	5,013
1132·1	46·5	17·1	3·5	8,102(b)
78	97	119	147	—
1680·9	34·8	8·4	1·2	1,324(a)
1711·5	19·3	8·7	1·9	2,151
1554·0	20·9	8·3	1·9	5,733(b)
93	60	99	149	—

(b) January 1950

to be brought from elsewhere and housed, with farmers who had never set a plough or drilled a field of corn. In five years the arable acreage was practically trebled, and three-fifths of it was under corn for the harvest of 1944 ; the newly ploughed pasture when drained, fertilised and limed grew two or three successive crops of wheat, barley and oats before there was need for a proper rotation to include roots and leys. In this process of converting grass to crop, sheep numbers fell by one-half and more in five years, with notable reper-cussions on the finances of the hill farms which bred them. For the first winter or two of war there was in these counties an acute problem of feeding the dairy cows and other cattle ; but once crop production had been successfully developed, fodder crops and the by-products of the corn enabled a larger number of cattle to be maintained with a considerable increase in milk production. Agricultural Executive Committees had in these counties to be both universal providers and ubiquitous teachers. They organised complete contract services for under-equipped farmers, and demonstrations in the techniques of arable cultivation and machine maintenance ; they were large employers of civilians and of Land Girls, housed in hostels, who could be loaned to farmers for potato planting and corn harvesting. The need for tractors and for all types of cultivating machinery was at its most urgent on these former grazing farms, whose pastures offered a magnificent reserve of fertility waiting to be tapped.

More specialised problems faced the dairy farmers in the north and west of England (Region IV). The cutting off of the supply of imported feedingstuffs jeopardised the output of milk and the subsidiary livestock enterprises such as pigs and poultry, which gave profitable returns in districts close to the great urban conglomerations in Lancashire and York-shire. Where good lowland grass was available the worst difficulties were overcome after 1941 by the production of corn, roots and kale for winter feeding ; with only one-third of the pre-war numbers of sheep and pigs, it became possible to grow more bread grains and potatoes as well as to keep rather more cows to offset the decline in the highest yields.

By the end of the war another problem had arisen on some Cheshire farms—the insufficiency of the remaining pasture to feed the dairy herd in a dry summer.

But many dairy farmers on the hills had no such reserves of pasture capable of conversion to more productive crops. They had been accustomed to feed cattle cake and oats all the year round, using their own land to provide hay, some grazing and exercise. At all times of the year their resources were inadequate to supply their herds ; their soil was often thin and infertile, their fields steep and stony ; there were neither horses, tractors nor implements for crop production. But crop production in some measure had to be forced upon them, and direct reseeding of old pastures to new and better yielding grass also proved a valuable help. Such measures, slowly developed over three or four years, raised the general standard of self-sufficiency on these farms, and milk yields gradually recovered from the drastic fall experienced in the first two winters of war. Yet with less to sell and heavy costs to be incurred in machinery and seeds, many of these farmers faced financial problems almost as acute as their technical ones. Their farms, economic in peace-time, became ' marginal ' in profitability in the conditions imposed by total war.

These highly specialised farms, like those devoted to pigs and poultry, were thus forced by war into a painful and unprofitable readjustment. For the many farms carrying on a mixed production—some crops, some pasture, most types of livestock—the war meant a change of emphasis. Fewer sheep and pigs, fewer pastures whether temporary or permanent, were succeeded by more bread grains and potatoes, more fodder crops for the cattle. The process can be traced in the statistics here given for Devon (Region V), a county characterised by small livestock farms on the valley sides and along the moorlands and by larger dairy and crop farms in the fertile lowlands. There were the general problems to be faced—the initial shortage of winter food, the conflict between the county quota for wheat and potatoes and the need of home-grown corn for the dairy herds, the allocation of a limited supply of tractors between farmers all in desperate need of more mechanical power. Similar adjustments were required at the other end of England, where the great sheep farms of the northern dales (Region VI) had similar problems of winter food for their cattle and sheep, and of mechanisation to grow more potatoes and oats in the fields which had for many years been down in pasture.

Intensified crop production and reduced livestock created for these mixed farms a serious unbalance in their labour. Farmers before the war had adjusted the various enterprises so as to provide full and regular employment for the staff they could house, with as little call as possible on outside casual help, other than that of neighbouring shepherds. More crops meant both a higher demand for labour and machinery all the year round and a greatly intensified seasonal peak, associated very largely with the potato. Lack of machinery and lack of labour, both regular and casual, was a serious hindrance in all these districts ; many of the extra workers drafted in were ' for the duration ' only, Women's Land Army, prisoners of war and the like for whom hostels had to be provided in large numbers. Shortages of phosphates and of lime were also serious matters when it came to cropping the hill-sides and rough pastures for the great harvests of 1943 and 1944 ; one corn crop, to satisfy the Agricultural Executive Committees' ' target,' could often best be followed by a carefully reseeded pasture which enabled some of the annual crop of lambs to be sold fat or which carried the cattle stock over the winter without starvation.

This problem, of winter food for livestock, was felt most acutely on the hill sheep farms, whose draft ewes, lambs not required for breeding and yearling cattle, were perforce sold each autumn to lowland farmers for fattening ; many of the young ewes also spent their first winter in the lowlands since the hill grazing was inadequate to supply both them and the breeding stock. But as pastures gave way to the plough, lowland flocks were sold and not replenished ; hill farmers found a poor demand for their livestock while the cost of wintering steadily rose. Those that employed hired workers found their outgoings increased by the successive changes in the minimum wage, but they derived little benefit from the controlled prices, since the greater part of their receipts came from livestock sold to other farmers and not to the Ministry of Food. After a decade of unprofitable prices, these upland stock rearers and mountain sheep farmers had few reserves with which to carry on until lowland flocks and herds were again increased ; their harsh climate and thin soils made any other type of husbandry unpracticable.

The moorland farms such as those in Northumberland and Durham (Region VI) often had some fields which could be ploughed out from gorse and bracken and put under fodder crops, oats or even potatoes ; with some reduction in sheep stocks, it might then be possible to fatten part at least of the annual crop of lambs and draft ewes. In such cases adjustment to war conditions hinged largely on finance—how to induce impoverished farmers to undertake the heavy costs of ploughing, fertilising and cropping land which was inherently infertile. For the mountain sheep farmers, the scope for adjustment was even narrower ; a reduction in sheep stocks only meant fewer sheep and less wool to sell with little reduction in general costs. The financial problems were correspondingly more acute, and as early as December 1940 a special subsidy was introduced for each ewe carried on hill sheep farms. As the war progressed this particular problem of financing ' marginal production ' in mountain and moorland regions became merged in the general discussions over profits, prices and costs to which we must now turn.

BIBLIOGRAPHY

Agricultural Statistics U.K. 1939–44, Part i (H.M.S.O. 1948) ; Part ii (H.M.S.O. 1949)
How Britain was Fed in War-Time (H.M.S.O. 1946)

CHAPTER VIII

THE FINANCE OF FOOD PRODUCTION, 1940-5

THE financial problems of food production in the first year of war have already been briefly mentioned. In order to secure greater output farmers were offered the orthodox inducement of higher prices, which were to lead, through an increase in their bank balances, to an increased input of fertilisers, seeds, machinery and workers, from whose combination was to come the increased output of crops. They were offered also guaranteed markets at these higher prices, so that the increased output would not result, as in pre-war years, in generally lowered prices or in a greater proportion of unsaleable stocks. If more was produced than could be consumed (as occurred with potatoes and carrots) the loss fell on the taxpayers who, as consumers, bought what they wished at the approved retail prices, and whose agents in the Ministry of Food paid farmers the guaranteed prices for the output unsold. These inducements towards increased output were certainly appropriate to the conditions of 1939, when there still existed unemployed labour, uncultivated land and idle capacity in the engineering trades, but these conditions changed rapidly in the second year of war.

Because price control was imperfectly formulated and inadequately applied in the first two years of war, the actual prices obtained by farmers gave a haphazard and irrational distribution of profits. Granted that a larger total of profits was required in 1939 and 1940 as an incentive to intensified output, its allocation between commodities and therefore between farming types was certainly unplanned. The margin for instance between average milk costs and the price paid was little if any wider in the first two years of war than in 1938–9 ; with falling milk yields and the loss of profitable side-lines, such as cream or eggs, the income of many dairy farmers probably fell in this period. On the other hand, prices of oats and barley more than doubled ; even allowing for the undue depression of cereal prices before the war, this ratio of increase was out of proportion to that shown for milk and potatoes.

The financial problems left over to the later years of war were therefore threefold : (1) the relation between total profits and total production in a fully employed economy ; (2) the distribution of profits, through the mechanism of prices, between different types of farming ; and (3) the relation between profits and the changing level of farm wages. In the final analysis, these three problems are one—the problem of ' incentive ' required to produce a given output from the varying conditions found in agriculture.

PROFITS AND PRODUCTION

Let us look more closely at this relationship between prices, profits and production. By raising prices all round in the summer of 1940 the Government increased by some £60 millions the gross returns of farmers from the sale of the crops and livestock grown in the early months of that year. By later price changes farmers' gross receipts rose in 1946 to £600 millions, compared with only £300 millions before the war.

How in fact did farmers use these increased sums ? The first reaction of many of them was to pay off the indebtedness to bankers or merchants incurred during twenty years of financial depression. Then there were the needs of their farms for more machinery, fertilisers, drainage and lime, to be bought at steadily rising prices. The cost of labour also rose steadily during the war. What was left, the amounts not spent on their farming operations, rose from some £60 millions before the war to nearly £200 millions in 1946. Some of this increase went in taxes ; the larger farmers especially paid back a high proportion of their extra receipts in excess profits tax. And there was real justification why farmers as a class should spend more on themselves and their families, since their incomes had undoubtedly been low before the war, low in relation to earnings in comparable occupations. Yet with all these allowances, the fact remains that farming income trebled in these years of war, a higher rate of increase than that shown probably by any other section of the community. Are we therefore to conclude that the prices for agricultural produce were too high from 1940 onwards, that the same result in production could have been achieved with a smaller increase in money incomes?

There are arguments which can be used to support this conclusion and others which tend in the opposite direction. There is in the first place the evidence of no less a person than the Chancellor of the Exchequer that the prices fixed did provide, for various reasons, higher profits than the Government had intended. The price settlement both of 1940 and of January 1942 gave farmers more by ' many millions ' than the contemporary calculations had foreshown, but the excess was left with farmers in order to maintain their goodwill towards the Government.[1] This excess arose from a number of causes (including the inevitable imprecision of these early attempts at ' planning '). The lack of a formulated policy meant that up till 1942 the Government was apt to alter prices individually and at short notice with inadequate attention to the ultimate results on the total income of the farming community. Prices were raised to induce earlier marketings of wheat, in a sudden panic over imports; to induce a quicker reduction in the number of pigs and of beef cattle; and as late as the autumn of 1941 sheep prices were again raised to induce arable farmers to keep more sheep in a mistaken fear over corn yields. Secondly, throughout all these years, farmers were successful in obtaining the increased output required with less resources than officials had expected. When feedingstuffs were rationed, farmers made better use of the grass and fodder crops; when wages rose, farmers overhauled their management and fitted in the extra plough-ing without taking on another man. Officials both of the Government and of the National Farmers' Unions were apt to forget that farmers, like other business men, will make

[1] House of Commons Debates, January 26 1944

better use of some essential commodity which has suddenly become dear or scarce.

The Government thus paid farmers more than was intended in the early years of war, more than the Government judged at the time to be strictly necessary to achieve the required level of output. And a supporting fact can be found in the very rapid increase in the prices offered by farmers for some desirable commodities which were also scarce. As long as there was unemployed labour, idle machinery and factories and undercultivated land, the increased financial demand from farmers resulted, as was intended, in an increased use of these factors. But that state of affairs was practically over by the end of 1940, when the rise in these prices began to attract attention. When all the agricultural engineering firms had orders in hand for a year's output, the value of second-hand machinery shot above the level of prices for the equivalent current model from the works. When skilled labour was fully employed, the level of wages rose sharply ; by the end of 1941, the minimum wage enforced in some of the English counties was 10s a week above the national minimum of 48s. (This inconvenient trend led, eventually, to the virtual abolition of the county Agricultural Wage Committees as described below ; these county minima were of course themselves often exceeded in the process of bargaining between individual farmers and their workers.) And finally, the value of agricultural land rose, especially the value of land which carried among other amenities the possession of a house. The famous dogma of Ricardo, that corn is not dear because rents are high, but rents are high because corn is dear, needed some modification to suit the Second World War. The inter-war legislation made it almost impossible for a landlord to raise the rent on a sitting tenant ; alone of the three agricultural partners, landlords obtained practically no increase in their incomes to meet the rising cost of living or the still steeper rise in the costs of maintenance deferred until after the war. It was the tenant-farmers and the owner-occupiers of good farm land who reaped all the Ricardian benefit from a period when corn prices were indeed high. The rise in the prices paid for farms with vacant possession, in the decade of the forties, will surely become a classic illustration of the effect of rising profits in forcing up the value of a factor of production whose supply is rigidly fixed. If farming profits had been lower, it is at least arguable that land and second-hand machinery would have been not less in quantity but lower in price, and the production of food would have been un-affected. And that point might perhaps be just as apposite to the agricultural expansion programme of 1947.

Let us now turn to the arguments which point to the other conclusion, that if profits had been appreciably less so also would production. In this connection, the dominating fact is that tremendous range in costs which characterises an industry based on land, and dependent more than any other on the detailed personal management of thousands of small units. For any type of agricultural production, the existence of increasing costs is a commonplace. If a sudden increase is required in the output of milk or wheat or oats, there must be brought into use land less suited for that product than that already so used, land which is more suited for some other type of production. To increase simultaneously most forms of agricultural output (with the exception of some relatively unimportant products) brings up at once the low yields and high costs per acre of much marginal land ; the sudden cutting off in 1941-2 of imported feedingstuffs meant an upheaval in the economy of many dairy farms that could only result in an immediate rise in costs. By some means or other the country had to pay the financial costs of this ' marginal ' production, since the food was required ; if prices had to cover this cost and leave some ' inducement ' to the marginal producer the better-placed farmer must inevitably reap greater profits.

The point can be illustrated from the detailed records of milk costs collected from dairy farmers in the eastern counties. Since the sample of farms is not identical throughout the period, small variations from year to year must be ignored, but the broad trends are clear. The average cost per gallon roughly doubled in five years ; the average profit per gallon increased in 1941–2 somewhat over the pre-war level, relapsed almost to that level in the two succeeding years and was not substantially increased until the last year of war.   But even more striking than the increase in average cost is the increase in the range of costs.   For each year results from the farms showing the ten highest costs and the farms showing the ten lowest costs have been averaged ; the difference between these two sets of average costs widened from about 9¼d per gallon in 1938–9 to nearly 14d per gallon in 1941–2, after which it again fell, temporarily, to the pre-war level.[1]   In other words, the ' marginal cost ' of the milk the country so urgently needed rose much more sharply than the average costs, since war-time changes in feeding were so much more drastic on some farms than on others.   This widening in the range of costs implied a corresponding trend in the range of profits derived from a uniform price for the product ; it might be argued that the total of profits must perforce be high in order to ensure an adequate return for the temporarily ' marginal ' producer.

This argument is closely linked with another, the need to include, in the element called profits, a substantial sum for investment in the tools required for the war-time output. An arable farmer in the eastern counties, it is true, had no urgent need for such investment in tractors or implements or barns ; he was only called upon to intensify his existing effort.   But a Leicestershire grazier or a dairy farmer in the pastures of Somerset and Dorset was called upon to transform his whole productive enterprise, just as factories making refrigerators were diverted to the production of tanks or air-craft.   In both cases, the basic tools had to be financed by the Government, directly or indirectly.   In the more important munition trades, the Government often provided the capital equipment on loan, or provided a substantial part of the financial cost in return for some control over its eventual dispersal if it became valueless for commercial use at the end of the war.   That process was administratively quite

---

[1] Figures by courtesy of the Farm Economics Branch, School of Agriculture, Cambridge

impracticable for the tens of thousands of small farms scattered
about the United Kingdom which might require new equipment ranging from a set of cultivating implements to a
complete installation of roads, fences, buildings, water pipes
and machinery. Here again it could be argued that it was
administratively simpler to be generous with prices, so that
most farmers would be able to buy what was wanted ; and
to be generous as well with Government pledges to maintain
a 'healthy and well-balanced agriculture' after the war,
leaving farmers to deduce that their newly acquired tools
would, for some years ahead, be earning profits sufficient to
pay their original cost and to leave something over.

The Distribution of Profits

There is much force in this general argument, that increased
profits can best be provided by a general increase in prices,
sufficient to cover the 'marginal costs' of the required increase
in production ; and that the profits earned by the more
fortunately placed farmers were simply part of the price which
the general public had to pay in order to get the food it
needed. But looking back at the early years of war after a
decade, it is the unintentional distribution of profits which is
so remarkable, the virtual absence, until a late stage, of any
direction to the farms where they might have the greatest
influence on production. And if profits had been differently
distributed, it is possible that the same production could have
been achieved with a smaller total.

The chief difficulty in this respect was the abrupt and
severe increase in cereal prices in the first two years of war.
This undoubtedly gave a stimulus to their production, but it
stimulated even more the profits of those farms with wheat,
oats and barley to sell ; the farms that grew crops for their
dairy cows had a far smaller return for their more arduous
task. Right up to 1944 two groups of East Anglian dairy
farms had farm incomes markedly below two groups of farms
selling mainly crops, either from a heavy clay soil or from the

chalk.[1] That disparity was partially recognised in January 1942, when it was agreed to impose a maximum price on malting barley from that harvest and to give a heavier weight to winter milk prices. The process had to be repeated two years later, when a special bonus was added to the milk price for the first 400 gallons sold per winter month and for the first 500 gallons sold in each summer month. But by then the level of cereal prices had been stabilised, and the only feasible adjustment was to raise milk prices to provide dairy farmers with profits comparable to those earned by the arable farmers ; social equity rather than financial economy was the determining influence.

And again, it should have been possible to apply sooner and more vigorously those special measures of discriminating price which favour the high-cost ' marginal ' producer whose efforts have to be encouraged in war-time. The price-plus-acreage-grant, for instance, was not applied to potatoes until 1941 and was only extended to wheat and rye from the 1943 harvest.[2] There seems no reason why that device should not

[1] Farm Economics Branch, School of Agriculture, Cambridge, *Report on the Economic Position of East Anglian Farming*, No. 35, 1949

[2] The arithmetic of this device is as follows :

		Total Receipts per acre
Farm A with yield of 8 tons of potatoes per acre : with price of £5 per ton with price of £3 10s per ton and grant of £10 per acre	£28 10	£40
		38
(equal to £4 15s per ton)		
Farm B with yield of 5 tons of potatoes per acre : with price of £5 per ton with price of £3 10s per ton and grant of £10 per acre	£17 10s 10	£25
		27 10s
(equal to £5 10s per ton)		

Thus Farm B gets a higher price per ton, which partly compensates for the lower yield per acre.

have been included in the 1940 price review, except that the officials and ministers had not then fully appreciated the economic problem which was developing.

Again, the ploughing grant of £2 per acre had been introduced early in 1939 to induce the early conversion of grassland to arable. That was a useful device for increasing the cash resources of exactly those farms which would have the greatest costs of conversion to war production. If cereal prices had been firmly controlled from the start with only a slight increase from the pre-war level, the ploughing grant might well have been multiplied three or four times at the outbreak of war, thus bringing about a quite different pattern of financial inducement with little administrative cost.

Allied forms of special grants were in fact substantially developed after 1943. By that time it was clear that a further increase in output could only be obtained from the upland farms for whose benefit most of these efforts were directed and whose profits were markedly below those obtained from the lowland farms. Consider for instance the general trends shown opposite by four groups of Scottish farms during the war.[1]

The hill sheep subsidy was historically the first of these special grants ; it was paid on the number of ewes of hill breeds kept in December of each year from 1940 onwards. In fact, the improved profits of these farms (modest as they were in comparison with those of other types) were very largely derived from this one subsidy. From 1943 onwards many of these farms also became entitled to the subsidy on hill cattle ; they could draw on the ' marginal production ' grants, which provided half the cost of approved works such as the application of lime and fertilisers, the purchase of better strains of

[1] D.O.A.S. 11th and 12th Economic Reports on Scottish Farming, 1946, 1947. As the sample of farms included was not constant from year to year, the figures can be regarded only as indicators of relative position. ' Net Income ' is defined as the excess of receipts over expenses, adjusted for valuation changes. It includes remuneration for the work of the occupier and his wife, or for interest on his capital and for interest payments on debts or mortgages.

AVERAGE NET INCOME PER FARM : SCOTLAND

	N.E. stock rearing	Arable and stock feeding	Dairy with arable	S.W. hill sheep	
				Total	including subsidy amounting to
	£	£	£	£	£
1938	176	—295	470	—	—
1939	344	1,206	1,056	7	—
1940	512	1,859	1,202	136	—
1941	823	2,288	1,369	514	377
1942	651	2,549	876	534	406
1943	823	1,768	1,087	717	331
1944	381	1,125	702	686	356

seeds either for crops or for resowing to grass, bracken clearing, fencing, and the like. It was in Scotland that these grants were most used during the war, to finance improvements of this sort on many small upland farms. The administration of these specific grants was undoubtedly heavy, but again it seems that their application was left too late to have maximum effect on the effort of war. All these measures designed to meet the high costs of the ' marginal ' producer forced into unfamiliar ways were useful and effective, but the final verdict must surely be that they were probably too little and certainly too late. They could but slightly rectify a mal-distribution of profits which handicapped the farmers from whom the greatest efforts were demanded, while it encouraged the pre-war arable farmer to unnecessary extravagance in the price he paid for machinery and pedigree livestock as a method of diminishing his Excess Profits Tax.

The two sections of this chapter have discussed briefly two economic problems of price policy in war-time ; they have been concerned with analysis rather than with chronology. To complete this account of agricultural prices a brief record may be useful of the sequence of price reviews during the war and their connection with agricultural wages.

WAGES AND PRICES

The changes made in the controlled prices of individual commodities during 1939–40 were consolidated in the summer of 1940, in that general upward lift of all prices [1] designed to meet the cost of the new minimum wage. The purpose of that wage increase, it will be remembered, was twofold. By removing the historical disparity between agricultural and industrial earnings, existing farm workers were to be compensated for the loss of their liberty to move into better paid occupations ; and the industrial unemployed would be more easily induced to take up work in agriculture.

The reasons for this historical differential between agricultural and urban wages may be traced far back into the nineteenth century, but whatever its origin it had become deeply embedded in the economic structure of the twentieth. By tradition, the social status of other groups in country districts, such as roadmen and porters on country railway stations, was largely judged from the higher wages and shorter hours of work than those enjoyed by the farm worker. A rise of 8s–10s a week in the general level of agricultural earnings thus disturbed the basis of the whole structure, which was quickly rebuilt on the old model. A study of wage differentials shows that within a year the pre-war margins between the rural occupations had been largely re-established at a correspondingly higher level [2] ; the main purpose of the wage increase made in June 1940 had thus been largely stultified by the determination of other groups of wage earners to maintain their relatively higher earnings.

This trend induced many of the county Agricultural Wage

[1] The commodities whose prices were left free were malting barley (though the price of feeding barley was controlled), all types of seed corn, poultry and vegetables other than potatoes. The prices of poultry, tomatoes, carrots and onions were brought under control between 1940 and 1942.

[2] *London and Cambridge Economic Service*, January 1946, p. 9. It should be noted that by the end of the war there were generally smaller margins between the lowest wages and those earned by craftsmen ; the unskilled labourers had improved their position both absolutely and relatively, together with the men employed in the pre-war depressed industries such as coal-mining and agriculture.

Committees to raise their own minimum rates in the autumn of 1941 ; and some coupled their decision with a formal request that the cost should be recouped to farmers by higher prices. This form of pressure on the Government by statutory bodies having only local authority was received with official disapproval ; with the consent of the trade unions and with only minor opposition from the farmers, the Minister of Agriculture eventually centralised all wage-fixing powers within the Wages Boards. But when both Boards, that for England and Wales and that for Scotland, raised the minimum wage to 60s a week at the end of 1941, the Government did undertake to review prices in accordance with its previous pledge.

The review was far more thorough than the rush and scramble of 1940. The higher prices required to meet the cost of the new wages were fixed so as to effect a substantial redistribution of the profits which had been made so unequally and so unexpectedly from the prices fixed in 1940. The Government proposed considerably higher prices for milk (especially for winter milk), and for potatoes and sugar-beet, two crops in whose production labour was a heavy cost ; there were to be small increases in the prices for cereals, fat cattle and sheep ; and nothing at all for pigs and eggs, whose output was inevitably falling with the loss of imported cereals, and whose prices were judged unduly high. When these decisions were made known, there was violent opposition from the National Farmers' Unions, which argued that all commodities should be given price increases equivalent to the effect on their average costs of the rise in wages. Apart from the imperfections of the available data on which to base such calculations, a mathematical relation between individual prices and costs would have made it impossible to rectify that unequal distribution of profits which had already taken place, or to alter the emphasis to be attached to the production of different commodities. But the final decision (which was largely to regulate prices from 1942 to 1944) provided for small increases in the prices of pigs and eggs, another ½d a gallon for milk and as a *quid pro quo* the control of malting barley prices from the harvest of 1942. In addition, the problems of financing ' marginal production ' without a general increase in prices were more firmly tackled by the measures mentioned above—a higher subsidy for hill sheep, a subsidy for hill cattle, grants for specific operations on upland farms, and an acreage grant for wheat and rye from 1943.

For eighteen months the minimum agricultural wage remained stable, though higher profits and the intensified shortage of men brought some rise in the wages farmers paid. Meanwhile, earnings outside agriculture continued to increase, for the same reasons. By 1943, as in 1941, there was a strong pressure to restore the traditional margins between farm and other wages, and the trade unions could justly complain that their members were still paid less than their probable earnings if they had been free to move to other occupations. In April the principle of the minimum wage (at 45s per week) was extended to include women working on the land ; overtime rates were also raised for both men and women, thus increasing the general level of earnings. Finally in December 1943 the English Wages Board declared a new minimum wage for adult men of 65s a week, in order to put agricultural and industrial earnings again on a more equal basis.

The failure of the Scottish Board to follow suit produced an awkward situation ; the English farmers promptly asked for a review of prices which necessarily applied to both parts of Britain, to the English farmers who paid the higher wages and to the Scottish ones who did not.[1] The Scottish District Wage Committees were on the whole opposed to a higher minimum wage ; it was not until they had been reduced, by Statutory Rule and Order, to the same level of ineffectiveness as their English counterparts, that the Scottish Wages Board was able in May 1944 to redress the inequality.

Meanwhile the Government's statisticians and economists had once more reviewed prices, costs and profits in the business of agriculture. Again it was found that farmers had received

---

[1] This situation was repeated in November 1950, when the Scottish Wages Board for some months delayed an increase in the minimum wage which had been granted in England and Wales.

considerably more than had been intended. Some of the excess was due to the superb harvest of 1942, and for that the Government disclaimed responsibility, for fear of inducing claims for lost income in a year of poor yields. But even with normal yields there would have been an excess, because farmers had in fact secured a greater output of livestock products than had been expected from the limited supplies of feedingstuffs, while mechanisation and improved management had partly offset the cost of the higher wages imposed in 1941. These improvements in efficiency the Government attributed in part to the missionary zeal of its Agricultural Executive Committees, whose milk production officers and technical experts had visited many farms which had hitherto had few contacts with scientific knowledge or even with the best farming of their district. Adding up the figures, Ministers found that the excess of profits thus earned by farmers over what had been intended was still large, larger indeed than the cost of the new wage. They decided therefore to make no increase in the general level of prices, holding that the increase in profits since the last review sufficiently fulfilled the spirit of its pledge, that farmers should be able to pay the approved level of wages. But it again emerged that profits were being made in the wrong places, and that the small dairy farmer in particular was underpaid for his arduous work. And it was agreed to raise still further the price of milk and to balance the total agricultural income by reducing the controlled price of malting barley by 2s 6d to 25s a cwt., a level at which it was still substantially above the prices of other cereals.

The review of prices early in 1944 thus resulted in a new division of the existing income in which some farmers gained slightly and others lost heavily, both by lower prices and higher wages. It is not surprising that this decision provoked a storm of resentment from the farmers who were given none of the figures on which it was based, but they were largely disarmed by the frank and courageous handling of Mr Hudson. The Minister of Agriculture rightly saw that behind the immediate issue lay the anxiety of the farmers over those problems of reconstruction and adaptation which would confront them at the end of hostilities. Would price control be continued ? Would there be a repetition of the fiasco of the old Agriculture Act, 1920, which was repealed just as the prices it guaranteed were engulfed in the post-war slump of 1920–3 ?

As a compromise on the immediate issue the Minister offered, on behalf of the Government, the ' temporary ' bonus on the first 400 gallons of milk sold by each farmer in each winter month, and on 500 gallons in each summer month. Secondly, he agreed that the National Farmers' Unions and the Agricultural Departments should jointly discuss the statistical methods used in these price reviews and the interpretation of the available data. And thirdly, it was generally agreed that these price reviews, developed haphazardly during the war, could usefully be continued into the post-war world to provide for farmers some guarantee of prices and of markets. They were to become an annual event, an annual examination of the prices, costs and profits of the agricultural community, undertaken jointly by the Agricultural Departments and the representatives of the farmers. Prices would then be fixed by the Government, taking into account these results, the programme for food production and all other relevant circumstances. For the four years from 1944 the existing prices were set as the guaranteed minimum at which the Ministry of Food would buy the whole output of milk, fat cattle, calves and sheep ; the actual prices would be fixed year by year, but would in no case be less than the minimum. Pigs and eggs were omitted from this guarantee for livestock products because their output depended so closely on the unpredictable supplies of imported cereals.

By the last winter of war, therefore, the farming community had obtained a general security of income to cover the post-war years, in return for the continued general direction by the Government over agricultural output. In this transitional period that direction would continue at two levels, by price inducement and, as a last resort, by legal compulsion applied through the Agricultural Executive Committees ; but as the urgencies of war faded it could reasonably be hoped that this would eventually be discarded.

But there remained the formidable task of inducing agriculture (along with other industries) to resume the pre-war habit of ' counting the cost.' Production, at almost any cost, had been demanded, and the desired output of food had been given at high cost. By the end of the war the Agricultural Executive Committees alone were spending more than £20 millions a year, partly offset by the sums farmers paid for the work of prisoners of war who were housed and fed from the accounts of the War Office. What would happen to the level of output when the prisoners went home and the Women's Land Army demobilised, when the committees could no longer loan machinery and gang labour at uneconomic charges in reply to a telephone call ? How soon could the pressure for bread grains and potatoes be relaxed ? How soon could the flocks and herds again be restored, it was to be hoped, with better bred animals giving a better performance ? Such problems for reconstruction dominated all the plans for British agriculture in that year between the landings in Normandy and the capitulation at Lüneberg.

BIBLIOGRAPHY

House of Commons Debates, Jan. 26 1944

Farm Economics Branch, School of Agriculture, Cambridge, Report No. 35, 1949

Economic Reports on Scottish Farming, 1946, 1947 (Department of Agriculture for Scotland)

London and Cambridge Economic Service, Jan. 1946

CHAPTER IX

RECONSTRUCTION AND FAMINE, 1944-6

FROM 1942 onwards the problems of post-war agriculture over-flowed the files in Whitehall. What, if any, of the administrative devices of war could usefully be carried over into the post-war world? What were the future prospects of the Agricultural Executive Committees and their many functions? What was to be done with the agricultural marketing boards which had been suspended in 1939 ' for the duration ' ? Was there to be a place for them and for the Ministry of Food? What were the prospects of obtaining for the British house-wives more food in greater variety?

It was not only in Whitehall that these problems were discussed ; in 1943 and 1944 almost every institution connected with agriculture produced a plan for it in the post-war world. These proposals disagreed on many things, but on two important points there was a remarkable coincidence of opinion. All the planners recommended that the system of guaranteed markets and guaranteed prices should be continued, as a permanent feature, for the main agricultural products ; and they all agreed that post-war farming should be based more on arable crops and less on pasture. Following Sir George Stapledon and his apostles, the planners were all for ley farming, for taking the plough round the fields, for a judicious rotation of the new Aberystwyth grasses and the new Cambridge cereals. It was also clear, even to unofficial planners, that the great increase in milk consumption implied a post-war dairy herd considerably greater than that existing in 1939.[1]

But although scientists and farmers could devise plans, only the Government could decide, and the Coalition Government that was to win the war against Germany was unwilling to embark on controversial blue-prints. It was necessarily

[1] See Menzies-Kitchin, A. W., *Future of British Farming* (Pilot Press, 1946), for a contemporary discussion of these post-war plans

left to the Labour Government which took office in July 1945 to formulate the administrative framework for post-war agriculture. But the understanding already reached with the National Farmers' Unions in 1944 provided for continued control over prices and markets until 1948 ; and the cropping policy for 1945 and 1946 had of course to be decided and announced in due season, irrespective of political changes during its execution.

CROPPING FOR 1945 AND 1946

As seen early in 1944 the prospects of securing quickly a better and more varied diet were not hopeful. For one or two years after liberation, Europe would need substantial quantities of bread grains from Allied resources ; it would be many years longer before European livestock could be restored to pre-war proportions, and Britain could again import condensed milk, bacon, cheese and eggs. There would also be immediate shortages in Europe of draught animals, machinery, fertilisers and seeds, and reserve stocks had to be accumulated from over-strained supplies ; beyond Europe loomed the unknown needs of Asia. For some years after the war, therefore, it would hardly be possible for Britain to lay claim to a greater part of the world's food supplies than that required to maintain a diet of austere proportions.

And when the fighting stopped, so also would Lend-Lease, and with it Britain's happy ignorance of the cost of imports. Before the United States entered the war, we had sold most of our foreign investments and thus greatly reduced our income of foreign exchange ; we had incurred a vast load of debt to other countries which would have to be repaid from our exports ; and during the war we diverted to its prosecution most of the equipment and personnel which had previously worked in the export trades. Internationally Britain had converted herself from a creditor to a debtor ; it was calculated that the volume of exports would have to be increased by 75 per cent of the pre-war level in order to provide the pre-war volume of imports, itself barely adequate for a larger and fully employed population.

The impending scarcity of foreign currencies with which to buy imports implied drastic measures both to reduce those imports to essentials only and to stimulate exports. Among these measures was the maintenance of a high level of food production at home, since imports of food were still a large item in the balance of payments. But there was also required a careful weighing of the relative advantages for this purpose of different forms of agricultural production. Meat, eggs, bacon and dairy products were expensive to buy ; the supply of a given quantity of meat and bacon could be provided with the least foreign exchange by importing animal feeds for conversion into animal products, using grass and other home-grown fodder as a supplement. A policy for the era of reconstruction had therefore three strands ; an increase in approved breeding stocks of animals to provide more dairy cows, beef cattle, pigs and hens ; the import if possible of more cereals and oilcake ; and a high production of crops both for direct human consumption and for the livestock.

The conclusions derived from these prospects were circulated to the Agricultural Executive Committees in the spring of 1944. As far as possible, still more pasture was to be ploughed to counter-balance the arable land now due to be put under grass. There could be as yet no relaxation in the output of sugar-beet and potatoes. The increased consumption of this latter crop implied some $1\frac{1}{4}$ million acres annually, a heavy burden compared with the pre-war 700,000 acres ; it remained to be seen whether potato consumption would fall as more alternative foods became available after the war. Eelworm infestation complicated the problem of allotting the required area among the counties, since the quota had to be reduced for the most important and worse affected districts in Lincolnshire and Lancashire. Some reduction in the area under wheat would be accepted in order to encourage the greater output of oats and other fodder crops to provide for the increased livestock and, it was hoped, for the rising output of milk.

For although imports of feeding grain could not be much increased in 1944–5, the Government was more hopeful over the prospects for wheat. At the end of 1943, the dilution of bread with barley and of beer with oats was stopped, and the extra feeding grain allotted to farrowing sows and to approved chick-rearing farms. A year later, in October 1944, the extraction rate for wheat was reduced by stages from 85 to 80 per cent ; the wheat offals provided from January 1945 a further increase in rations for pigs and poultry, a special allowance for heifer calves, and the steady increase in the consumption of rationed feeds by dairy farmers to support the greater volume of milk.

By the summer of 1945 the planned revival of livestock husbandry was thus gathering momentum. The number of pigs was up by one-sixth of its lowest level ; poultry on agricultural holdings increased from 51 millions in 1943 to 62 millions ; the slow increase in cattle numbers continued. Only flocks of lowland sheep showed no revival ; folded flocks on arable land meant too much work and grazing flocks competed with the dairy cows. And for the first time the area under crops showed a substantial fall ; the wet autumn of 1944 and the relaxation of pressure for wheat resulted in a drop of almost one million acres for this crop, which was only partly offset by more barley and oats ; more than 600,000 acres had been added to the area under temporary grass.

This shift from crops for sale to crops for animals was further emphasised by the price settlement of February 1945, the first of the annual reviews held under the new procedure. It was also a ' special ' review, for there had been once again an increase in the minimum wage for farm workers (to £3 10s a week) in order, once again, to reduce the revived disparity between rural and urban wages. There was to be a higher price for milk (from April 1945) and for fat stock and eggs (from July 1945). An increase of 10s a ton for potatoes and of 5s a ton for sugar-beet of the current harvest was to be withdrawn in 1946 if compulsory directions to grow these crops could then be stopped ; and in the same case it was agreed that the acreage grant for wheat and rye could also be halved.

There was also to be a lower minimum price for barley, a price which was still out of line with those of other cereals. These adjustments, actual and prospective, meant a further shift in incomes from the cash-cropped farms to those more dependent on livestock.

And with this price settlement was also largely determined the cropping policy for 1946—no compulsory directions, it was hoped ; more milk and more livestock ; a greater production of animal fodder from improved grass ; and the welcome appearance, on a small scale, of imported maize to supplement the rations for hens and cows. For the policy of the last eighteen months had brought a heavy commitment in a larger number of grain-consuming animals (especially pigs and hens) for whom basic rations would have to be provided by the Ministry of Food. Within a few weeks of VE day, that Ministry issued a warning (so cautiously that it was barely audible) that it might not be able to supply the extra cereals required. Stocks of cereals accumulated during the war diminished with alarming speed in 1945, because European wheat production was barely half the pre-war level and because there was a record number of animals on North American farms. By the autumn of 1945 it was doubtful if all the animals in America and Europe could be fed ; by the early weeks of 1946, after prolonged droughts in India and South Africa, it was clear that all the human beings could not be fed.

It was a new Government which had to cope with the food shortage now threatening, but the political change had remarkably little effect on immediate agricultural policy. Mr Hudson, Minister of Agriculture since May 1940, was succeeded in that office by his Parliamentary Secretary, Mr Tom Willlams, who was thus already acquainted with the plans for post-war agriculture which he had helped to formulate. The administrative structure for farming in the future was announced in November 1945, and preparations for the necessary legislation went on in Whitehall offices, but the chief interest over the winter of 1945–6 did not lie in parliamentary bills. The Ministry of Food, following the warnings of the Combined Food Board, made cautious statements on the rapid disappearance of cereal stocks ; the Minister of Agriculture warned farmers that cereal production could not safely be relaxed in this country, even though there would be no compulsion and a lower acreage grant for wheat. Nevertheless in November 1945 the rations for pigs and poultry on agricultural holdings were raised to supply one-quarter instead of one-sixth of the pre-war numbers, and a further increase was promised for the early spring.

It was therefore with consternation that the House of Commons heard a few weeks later that British imports of cereals would necessarily be reduced below the planned level in the first half of 1946, and that the deficiency would have to be made good by raising the wheat extraction rate to 85 per cent immediately and to 90 per cent shortly. Instead of being increased, all feedingstuff rations would be sharply reduced in May, and by July the rations for pigs and poultry were indeed back to the lowest level of the war years, calculated to supply barely one-twelfth of pre-war numbers. And in this last month, bread and flour were rationed, a step which had been avoided in the darkest days of the Battle of Britain or the Battle of the Atlantic.

In the parliamentary debates the chief target for criticism was not the actual cut in feedingstuff rations ; with the absolute scarcity of cereals, smaller imports and higher extraction rates were accepted as inevitable, together with the abrupt reversal of the trend in livestock numbers. But there were some very pointed comments about the promise to raise feedingstuff allowances made at the end of the year, when the existence of a world famine should already have been known to, and appreciated by, the Goverment. Later events—the droughts in India and South Africa which sent these countries into the world markets as desperate buyers—only confirmed what should, it was argued, have been proclaimed before the end of 1945 ; that cereals were needed to keep humans alive rather than to provide a smaller quantity of more palatable food in the form of livestock products.

By February it was also too late for any appeals to have much effect on the cropping for the 1946 harvest. Farmers were indeed urged to plant as much spring wheat as possible, but the Minister firmly refused to restore the acreage grant to the previous £4, arguing that a change in price should never be made except as part of a co-ordinated review of all prices. Such a review had in fact to be undertaken at mid-summer, on the award by the Wages Board of a further 10s a week in the minimum wage rate.

An earlier decision of the Wages Board taken in February raised women's wages (by 2s to a minimum of 50s a week), increased over-time rates for all workers and reduced the hours to which these wages applied to a uniform 48 per week all the year round. These extra costs were one element considered in the second of the annual price reviews under-taken in February 1946 which revealed a declining trend in agricultural profits. Farmers had then received an estimated £16 millions annually in the form of higher prices for livestock and livestock products (from April or July 1946), and for potatoes and sugar-beet from the 1946 harvest ; slight increases in the prices for wheat and oats were offset by yet another reduction in the minimum price for malting barley. The new wage increases, coupled with the general disturbance of production plans since the cereal famine developed, led to a fresh review of agricultural output and incomes as a whole.

Basing its calculations on the increased costs of wages paid to hired workers, the Government allocated increases in agricultural prices calculated to raise gross receipts of farmers by some £17 millions a year. In reversal of the price emphasis made in February, most of this sum was provided by higher crop prices, both for the 1946 and 1947 harvests ; apart from an extra 1d per gallon for milk, the livestock prices were increased relatively less. But as compensation for the shortage of feedingstuffs, special and temporary grants were given, of 2d per gallon for sales of milk in three winter months ; of £4 per head for sows farrowing in August, September and October (for whose progeny there might not be adequate food); of a somewhat higher price for light-weight pigs, and for eggs sold in August–November.

The National Farmers' Unions objected strongly both to

the total sum awarded and to the method of its distribution between commodities. They argued that labour costs should include an allowance for the manual work of farmers to be valued at the new minimum wage, and that therefore a sum of some £25 millions was required. The Government had no difficulty in demolishing that argument, for farmers are remunerated from profits, not from wages. Farmers who did not employ hired workers gained from the higher prices; those with large farms (who were managers rather than manual workers) would admittedly not receive the full recoupment of their extra costs, but (as the Government and the National Farmers' Unions agreed at a later date) it was quite impossible to adjust prices of national application to suit the individual circumstances of hundreds of thousands of farmers. And on the second point the Government firmly reserved the right to alter the price emphasis between commodities at their own discretion, but admitted that such alteration should normally be confined to the annual review in February.

The world food shortage which necessitated this change in price emphasis had been discovered too late in the season to affect appreciably the cropping for 1946; only for potatoes and vegetables grown on farms was there a slight increase in acreage. Otherwise the total area under crops continued to decline and the area under temporary grass continued, slowly, to increase:

AREA OF CROPS IN UNITED KINGDOM

	1939	1944	1945	1946
	Thousand Acres			
Wheat	1,766	3,220	2,274	2,062
Barley	1,013	1,973	2,215	2,211
Oats	2,427	3,656	3,753	3,567
Potatoes	704	1,417	1,397	1,423
Sugar-beet	345	431	417	436
Total Tillage	8,813	14,548	13,849	13,300
Temporary Grass	4,093	4,725	5,334	5,679
Total Arable	12,906	19,273	19,183	18,980
Permanent Grass	18,773	11,735	11,840	12,030
Total Crops and Grass	31,679	31,008	31,023	31,010

CHAPTER X

THE ADMINISTRATIVE FRAMEWORK FOR POST-WAR AGRICULTURE

DURING the years 1947 and 1948 five Acts of Parliament framed the permanent policy for agriculture that had been announced by the Labour Government in November 1945. The Agriculture Act, 1947, gave legislative sanction for the annual price review and the twin principles of guaranteed prices and guaranteed markets for the most important farm products. The Agricultural Holdings Act, 1948, and the Agriculture (Scotland) Act, 1948, brought up to date the law relating to landlord and tenant, and incorporated the new ideas on the enforcement of minimum standards of efficiency in the use of agricultural land. The Hill Farming Act, 1946, passed at the end of that year, continued and expanded the measures of rehabilitation already applied to this depressed branch of agriculture. The Agricultural Wages (Regulation) Act, 1947, made permanent that transference of power from the local Wage Committees to the two Wage Boards which had been effected in the course of the war.

The details of this legislation can be followed in the references given and need not be described here. But it is interesting to note how closely this post-war framework follows the pattern of administration evolved during the war ; and it is important to note in what general terms this legislation has been drafted, how wide a scope it leaves to the discretion of the administrators.

AGRICULTURE ACT, 1947

' The twin pillars upon which the Government's agricultural policy rests are stability and efficiency. The main method of providing stability is through guaranteed prices and assured markets.' In furtherance of this policy laid down in the Explanatory Memorandum, the Agriculture Act made it obligatory on the agricultural ministers to hold annual reviews into the general economic condition and prospects of agriculture, in consultation with representatives of producers. As a result of these reviews prices were to be fixed for the crops to be harvested eighteen months ahead ; minimum prices for fat stock, milk and eggs were to be fixed for a period of two to four years ahead, and actual prices for the year beginning after the completion of the price review. The Ministers can also, at their discretion, hold a special review if there has been, in their opinion, a substantial change in costs. The prices fixed can be calculated in any way thought best, such as a price for a given quality ; as a deficiency payment related to a standard price ; or as an acreage payment. The Act further authorises the Ministers to relate any price to a specific quantity of any home-grown product, but provides that at least one year's notice (and if possible more) should be given before quantitative limitation is applied to any market. The products included in the operation of this Act are fat stock, milk, eggs, wheat, barley, oats, rye, potatoes and sugar-beet ; wool was added in 1950.

There is nothing in this Act which in any way limits the freedom of the Government to fix any price at any level, at its own discretion, provided due notice has been given of the change. The prices are not tied (as were those of the Agriculture Act, 1920) to the ascertained average cost of production ; the Government is not committed to establish any precise ' parity ' between industrial and agricultural prices, on the American model. The Act provides not a policy but a piece of administrative machinery which can be put to diverse uses.

Although legislation has not limited the absolute discretion of the Government in making its annual (or special) reviews of agricultural incomes, there is a general agreement with the National Farmers' Unions on the type of data presented at them. First, there are calculations on the net income of the farming community in the recent past—the total receipts of farmers less their expenditure on production. Secondly, there are estimates of the average net income per farm for groups of farms of varying size and type. And thirdly, there are estimates of the changes since the last price review in average costs of producing the main commodities, and of the changes likely to occur from any foreseen movement in costs, such as a rise in minimum wages.[1] The basis for this last type of calculation is the analysis of many hundreds of farm accounts made each year by the Advisory Economists to show the cost structure of the main commodities—for instance, the proportion of milk costs provided by expenditure on rent, purchased feedingstuffs, labour, machinery and fertilisers. If labour is found to compose 40 per cent of the total cost of producing a gallon of milk, and a 10 per cent increase in wages is expected, it can be calculated that the increase in average costs of milk production will be about 4 per cent. That average increase will occur, of course, on only a small number of farms ; many will have labour costs above the average, and roughly as many will have labour costs below the average, but a price review cannot deal with individual farms. It should also be noted that it is the percentage change in costs from one period to another which is important for this purpose, not the absolute level of each year's average cost whose relationship to the average price is too indefinite to be useful.

These statistics are examined for the light they throw on farm costs, on the aggregate farm income, and on the distribution of that income between types and sizes of farms. The agricultural Ministers have then to decide what aggregate farm income is desirable, and what changes in the general price level are required in order to produce it. (Up to 1947 it appears that a figure of about £200 millions had been accepted between the Government and the National Farmers' Unions as a desirable level of aggregate farm income, but after the agricultural expansion programme of that year the figure rose to nearly £300 millions.[2]) Finally, a decision has to be made on the required output of the different products

[1] Heath, W. E., ' Price Fixing Policies,' in *Journal, Agricultural Economics Society*, December 1947
[2] 'National Income and Expenditure of the United Kingdom, 1946 to 1949,' p. 14, Cmd. 7933, 1950

and on the changes in the individual prices which may be necessary to induce that output. When the output of live-stock was to be especially encouraged, as in February 1946, their prices were increased by a considerably greater propor-tion than was warranted by the change in their calculated average costs ; while the prices of crops received an upward adjustment which was smaller than the calculated change in their costs. Six months later, after a rise in the minimum wage and the realisation of a world food shortage, this price emphasis was reversed ; crops for sale (especially bread grains) obtained a higher proportionate increase in price than was allotted to livestock and livestock products.

In addition to the market prices paid for the output of crops and livestock, the Government has made use of other methods of allocating income to certain types or sizes of farm or for certain forms of expenditure. The annual subsidy for each ewe and for some types of cattle kept on hill farms has assisted the profits of these farms which sell, not crops and livestock to the Ministry of Food, but store and breeding stock to other farmers. The milk bonus paid from 1944 on a stated minimum quantity of milk sold per month was expressly designed for the benefit of the small dairy farms. In the summer of 1946, as compensation for the unexpected shortage of feedingstuffs, special and temporary additions were made to the prices of milk, light pigs and eggs, and there was a special payment for farrowing sows ; in the summer of 1947 special acreage payments were offered for crops sown on land which had been subjected to floods in the spring of that year. As well as these temporary and compensatory payments for various abnormal costs, farmers can claim grants in aid of the cost of certain stated improvements, usually at the rate of one-half of the cost. These grants cover field drainage, water supplies, the application of lime, and the general improvement in hill land and in land classed as ' marginal.' They are legally based not on the Agriculture Act, 1947, but on the Hill Farming Act, 1946, and on other special legislation.

The Agriculture Act, 1947, with its associated legislation thus provides a comprehensive framework which can be used for any form of price determination thought best by the Government of the day. In a period dominated by a shortage of food, British farmers have obtained a legally assured market for all their output, at prices which were insulated from the equivalent prices of imported foods and from the retail prices at which consumers bought. But they certainly did not, in the post-war years, obtain stable prices. Crop prices for 1947–8, for instance, were fixed in February 1946; they were substantially increased in June 1946 after an increase in the minimum wage, when special emphasis was placed on the need for bread grains; a small increase was awarded in February 1947; the spring sown cereals were given a special price incentive in April 1947 to compensate farmers for the reduced yields expected from the late sowings; and there was a final adjustment in August 1947 after another increase in the minimum wage. Stability in agricultural prices depends both on stability in policy, which was inevitably unattainable in these years, and also on stability in the general level of prices and wages which has still not been achieved.

Standards of Efficiency

The annual price review and the bulk purchase of the major farm products by the Ministry of Food were jointly to provide British agriculture with stability. To secure efficiency in the post-war world, the Government relied on a nationally organised advisory service, linked with Agricultural Executive Committees on the war-time pattern.

Between the wars technical advice for farmers in England and Wales had been provided as part of the educational services organised by the county councils. As noted earlier, there was a wide range in the scope and efficiency of the technical services then available to farmers; the purely agricultural counties, with a low rateable value, tended to have fewer staff than the counties with industrial or residential areas. And only a few farmers availed themselves of the facilities thus provided; in every county the agricultural organiser and his staff had been consulted only by a minority, mainly the more progressive men.

One of the great achievements of the war was to bring agricultural science into touch with the problems of production on every farm. Wireworm surveys, soil analyses, cropping programmes, grants for field drainage or for ' marginal production,' falling milk yields or poor quality milk, all these took the technical experts on to farms and fields in the cause of greater output. And the association in the Executive Committees of technical experts with local residents, unpaid volunteers in the same cause, created a healthy public opinion on the responsibility of the farming community as a whole for securing at least a minimum level of efficiency in the management of land. Early in the post-war plans the Coalition Government had decided to continue this expanded technical service on a permanent basis ; it secured legislation setting up an Agricultural Advisory Service directly responsible to the Ministry of Agriculture.[1]

The Labour Government which came into power in 1945 decided to continue also the Agricultural Executive Committees in each county, to which the National Agricultural Advisory Service was to be attached. (In Scotland the Agricultural Executive Committees are distinct from the Agricultural Advisory Committees, which exercise a general supervision over the provision of technical advice to farmers.) The new committees were to consist, as before, of unpaid local residents, nominated by the Minister partly from names submitted by the bodies representing farmers and landowners. In addition to the technical staff provided by the Agricultural Advisory Service, these committees still required a considerable executive branch for all the administrative functions that continued even when the war ended—the rationing of feedingstuffs, fertilisers and some machinery ; grants for land drainage and water supplies ; the management of land requisitioned during the war ; the contract services for farmers, such as ploughing, pest control, crop spraying, gang labour for harvesting.

These Executive Committees were also charged with the ultimate sanction for securing efficiency—the dispossession of

[1] Agriculture (Miscellaneous War Provisions) Act, 1944

the inefficient. During the war the occasional exercise of this drastic power had been accepted by public opinion, although with reluctance, as a necessary evil in order to avert a still greater evil—a shortfall in food production. By the Agriculture Act, 1947, the Agricultural Holdings Act, 1948 and the Agriculture (Scotland) Act, 1947, the powers of the agricultural ministers in this matter were more clearly defined ; and one great objection to the war-time practice was met by providing a right of appeal. Every occupier of agricultural land, whether a tenant or an owner, is now required to ' maintain a reasonable standard of efficient production ' ; every owner of agricultural land is required to manage it so as ' to enable the occupier of the land to maintain an efficient standard of production.'

Where these obligations are not being carried out three measures can be used. The agricultural Ministers have powers to direct that certain fixed equipment shall be provided, or shall be repaired. Secondly, an occupier or a landowner can be placed formally under the supervision of the appropriate Agricultural Executive Committee for one year. Only if no satisfactory improvement has been shown during that year, or if directions given during supervisions have not been executed, do the Ministers have powers to dispossess. But an appeal can then be made against dispossession to one of the Agricultural Land Tribunals established in England and Wales for this purpose, or to the existing Land Court in Scotland.

The agricultural Ministers can thus acquire land which is being inefficiently farmed or managed, and having acquired it, they can either retain it or arrange for a new tenant. But in addition the Ministers can acquire land compulsorily where ' full and efficient use cannot be made of it for agricultural purposes without the provision of equipment or the carrying out or maintenance of works which could only reasonably be expected to be undertaken by the State.' Included in this provision is land acquired during the war, which can thus be retained permanently in the control of the State, notwithstanding any agreement for its eventual return to the original owners. Here again, an appeal against acquisition or retention can be made to the Agricultural Land Tribunals or the Scottish Land Court, and a number of such appeals were subsequently made against the proposed retention of land which had been acquired under war-time powers.

A further extension of war-time practice was embodied in the Hill Farming Act, 1946, which generally followed the recommendations of the two committees set up to investigate the chronically depressed state of hill sheep farming.[1] In addition to the existing sheep and cattle subsidies, provision was made for grants (up to half the cost) in aid of comprehensive schemes for land improvement on hill farms, submitted either by owners or by tenants. By this means it was planned to restore some of the capital drained from these areas by a decade of financial loss and to improve the amenities available to the farmers and workers. Great use has been made of these provisions in Scotland, with its large areas of hill and mountain grazing, and schemes of land improvement with a total cost of nearly £3 millions had been submitted to the Department of Agriculture for approval up to the end of 1949. It is much to be hoped that careful records will be kept of the benefits eventually derived from these State-aided schemes, whether in the form of extra output from these grazings or of improved earnings to the occupiers.

The post-war legislation thus put on to a permanent basis the administrative measures which had been evolved to meet the urgencies of war. But one section of the Agriculture Act 1947 went far beyond any war-time legislation.[2] Clause 31 provided that a tenant of an agricultural holding who receives a notice to quit may object and appeal to the Minister ; the notice to quit shall not then take effect without the consent of the Minister, who in making his decision will only consider

[1] 'Report of the Committee on Hill Sheep Farming in Scotland,' Cmd. 6494 ; 'Report of the Committee on Hill Sheep Farming in England and Wales,' Cmd. 6498 (H.M.S.O. 1944)

[2] This, and other clauses dealing with tenant right, compensation for disturbance and for improvements, arbitration over rent etc., were consolidated with previous legislation in the Agricultural Holdings Act, 1948 ; the equivalent for Scotland is embodied in the Agriculture (Scotland) Act, 1948.

whether the change in occupation is likely to result in more efficient cultivation. The trend in half a century of legislation has thus come to its logical conclusion ; tenant farmers who were granted in 1883 at least one year's notice before quitting have now been converted virtually into tenants for life, irrespective of the terms of their existing leases. Doubts have already been expressed whether this absolute security of tenure to all except the conspicuously inefficient is really in the best interest of the farming community. No landlord can now remove a tenant of only moderate standards in order to give a chance to the young man of promise and energy.

Indeed, taken in conjunction with current taxation, this legislation may very drastically affect the willingness of landlords to continue their function, since a farm once let has virtually passed out of the control of its owner. If large estates continue to be sold, and private landowners prefer to reap the profits of farming as owner-occupiers of a smaller area, the would-be tenant farmer, with limited capital, may reluctantly be forced into the expense of ownership. There will then be few farms to let, mainly from corporate bodies such as the Crown Commissioners, County Councils or the Agricultural Land Commission. This body was set up under the Agriculture Act 1947 to manage land acquired permanently by the Ministry of Agriculture and may in time become an important landowner of this sort. Before the Second World War one-third of the agricultural land in Great Britain was in fact farmed by owner-occupiers and it seems probable that before long that proportion will be considerably higher.

The purpose of these particular Acts was to secure a minimum level of efficiency in the cultivation of farm land, by giving security of tenure to tenant farmers who attain that minimum level, and by removing farmers, whether tenants or owners, who are obviously inefficient. But the immediate post-war years also saw the extension of State control over the general use of all land, through measures of town and country planning and through nationalisation of land values which may arise from a change in that use. This legislation lies outside the scope of the present book which is concerned with the story of agricultural land.

Agricultural Marketing

The Agriculture Act provided markets and a mechanism of price-fixing for the staple products of British farming, but it left unanswered a number of questions about the processes of marketing. During the war the responsibility of farmers for their output ended at the first point of delivery—the packing station for eggs, the grading centre for fat stock, the farm gate for milk. There were certain minimum standards of quality to be observed, but the agreed prices made little attempt to reward those who achieved higher levels. Scarcity and rationing emphasised the importance of quantity, to be obtained at the expense of quality and variety. But when scarcity was mitigated and rationing relaxed, would not consumers again demand a nice adjustment of supplies to their preferences ? Was the satisfaction of that demand to be left entirely to the Ministry of Food, or were producers to regain the responsibility for marketing that they had lost with their marketing boards ?

At the end of the war the four Milk Marketing Boards were in active existence, but their constitutions had been considerably modified. In directing the distribution of milk at the wholesale stage, they acted as agents of the Ministry of Food ; in negotiating milk prices with the Agricultural Departments, they acted as agents of the producers under the powers obtained from the Agricultural Marketing Acts. The Hops Marketing Board alone continued to operate entirely under the pre-war legislation. The boards for potatoes, pigs and bacon had been suspended in 1939 ; they remained legally in existence, they held considerable funds, but they were totally inactive. Should these boards be revived in their entirety ? What part could they play in the marketing of those commodities which were included in the price-fixing mechanism of the Agriculture Act ? Would marketing boards still be of value to the growers of products without that guarantee—wool, hops, fruit and vegetables ?

The Government remitted these controversial matters to a committee under the chairmanship of Lord Lucas, and asked for a report on the working of the Agricultural Marketing Acts up to 1939, and on any modification in their provisions which might be desirable in the light of post-war policy for food and agriculture. Another committee investigated with a similar aim the wholesale distribution of milk as it had evolved during the war.

The Lucas Committee felt that the marketing boards ought to be reduced in scope if they were to be fitted into the post-war framework. They had been designed primarily to obtain for farmers higher prices after the catastrophic fall from 1929 onwards. Their powers to limit output (as for hops) or to fix retail prices (as for milk) had been severely criticised even before the war, and were quite inappropriate as long as the Ministry of Food provided markets and the Agricultural Departments negotiated prices. The Committee felt that producer-controlled boards might be useful for the early stages of marketing—for grading, packing or transport, but it recommended that they should in future be limited to such functions. In the opinion of the Committee it was ' utterly wrong to allow a single sectional interest or combination of sectional interests to exercise monopoly rights ' over the marketing of produce bought by the taxpayers.

Not did the Committee have much confidence in the ability of the Ministry of Food to secure economic marketing in the post-war world. It paid tribute to the success achieved during the war in securing fair shares for consumers, and also fair shares for distributors ; much trouble had been taken in allotting to each firm its pre-war proportion of the total trade in, or total income derived from, each group of products. The Ministry had also eliminated some unnecessarily complicated transport, especially in the case of milk ; both retail rounds and wholesale transport had been drastically simplified. But the Committee judged the Ministry to be ' too distributor minded ' to continue the search for lowered distributive costs which might involve still more drastic changes in established customs and margins.

The principal recommendation of the Lucas Committee was that the Government should establish a series of Commodity Commissions, responsible only to the taxpayer, in order to supervise and if necessary organise the marketing of agricultural products from the time they left the marketing boards until they reached the retailer. The same conclusion was reached by the Williams Committee, which also recommended that a statutory body, independent both of dairy farmers and of the existing distributors, should be solely responsible for the transport, processing and distribution of milk from the first point of collection until it reached the nation's doorsteps.

This surprising consensus of opinion did not evoke an enthusiastic response from the Government. It was then engaged in setting up boards to run the newly nationalised industries—coal, electricity, gas and transport ; it may well have shrunk from thrusting further controversial legislation on an over-worked Parliament and civil service. Ministers announced that the reports of these two committees were being carefully considered, a process which was apparently continuing beyond the end of the decade. The only positive result was the Agricultural Marketing Act, 1949, which modified the provisions of the two earlier Acts, so as to secure more Government nominees on the boards and to give the agricultural Ministers stronger powers to control their operations.

During 1950 two new marketing boards were established, the first for tomatoes and cucumbers, which were not included in the price-fixing machinery of the Agriculture Act. The second was for wool, which the Government promptly added to the schedule of that Act, apparently as a reward to producers for having formed a marketing board. The logic of this action was not explained to the general public, and it remains among the mysteries of high agricultural policy. The fate of the suspended boards has not yet been announced, nor have the dual responsibilities of the Milk Marketing Boards been satisfactorily resolved.

BIBLIOGRAPHY

Agriculture Bill, Explanatory Memorandum, Cmd. 6996, 1946 ; *Agriculture (Scotland) Bill, Explanatory Memorandum*, Cmd. 7175 ; *Rights and Obligations of Landlords, Tenants and Owner-Occupiers of Agricultural Land*, 1949 ; *Agriculture in Scotland, The Report of the Department of Agriculture for Scotland for 1939-1948*, Cmd.7717, 1949

Report of the Committee on the Working of the Agricultural Marketing Acts (H.M.S.O. 1947)

Report of the Committee on Milk Distribution, Cmd. 7414 (H.M.S.O. 1948)

Report of the Committee on Hill Sheep Farming in Scotland, Cmd. 6494 ; *Report of the Committee on Hill Sheep Farming in England and Wales*, Cmd. 6498 (H.M.S.O. 1944)

CHAPTER XI

AGRICULTURAL EXPANSION, 1947-9

THE year 1947 was remarkable both for its climate and its economic events. The impact on agriculture of the exceptional weather was immediate and direct. Between three and four million sheep were lost on hill farms from the prolonged snow ; a sudden thaw brought heavy floods over some 300,000 acres of ploughed land, and delayed the planting of spring crops. Late frosts and a drought kept back the growth of crops and grass ; yields were substantially below the decennial average, and a yield of less than six tons of potatoes to the acre led directly to the rationing of that staple food in the autumn of 1947. Bread had been rationed since the middle of the previous year, so that purchases of both the principal sources of carbohydrates were limited over the winter of 1947–8.

The economic climate was also harsh and tempestuous. For two years the American loan had supported the level of British imports, while British exporters restored their factories, accumulated machinery and raw materials, regained their workers and rebuilt their overseas connections. In July the pound was again made freely convertible into other currencies just as the diminished harvests emphasised the continued dependence of European countries on North America. The demand for dollars with which to buy food and raw materials thus became canalised on to sterling ; within a few weeks the American loan was exhausted, gold reserves depleted, and at the end of August the pound was once more ' inconvertible ' except under strict control.

The generous promise of ' Marshall Aid ' held hopes that the flow of goods from the United States would not be immediately blocked ; meanwhile, drastic measures were devised to balance British imports against the rising but still inadequate level of British export..

PROGRAMME FOR AGRICULTURE

During the war the task of British farmers was to save ships by producing the bulky foods, bread grains, potatoes, vegetables and milk. In August 1947 they were asked to save imports by producing more of everything, with emphasis on the foods expensive in dollars, such as livestock products. Within five years agriculture was to expand its net output by 20 per cent of the current level, or by one-half of the pre-war level. At current prices the decision meant that net output should by 1951-2 have increased by £100 millions over 1946-7, when the net output of British agriculture was estimated at £500 millions.

This programme implied an output of crops nearly equal to that achieved at the peak of the war, about $13\frac{1}{2}$ million acres, compared with $14\frac{1}{2}$ millions in 1943-4, and not quite 9 millions in 1936-8. Combined with this crop production was to be an output of livestock and livestock products very considerably greater than before the war and far greater than in 1943. It was hoped to increase egg production by one-half, compared with 1936-8 ; milk sales by one-quarter, beef production by one-tenth ; and to raise the output of pig meat and of mutton nearly to the pre-war level.

How was this expanded output to be achieved ? The Government's answer—a further increase in farm prices and farming incomes—had at least the merit of simplicity. In July 1947 the minimum wage for farm workers had again been raised (by 10s to £4 10s a week), and the agricultural Ministers were therefore engaged at this time in a special review of farm costs and incomes. Over and above the increase in prices required to pay the higher wages, estimated at £18 millions annually, a further rise in prices was granted to induce the required expansion in output. The general level of agricultural prices was raised by some 15 to 20 per cent ; to encourage cattle breeding there were to be grants for every calf reared ; to encourage cropping there were to be grants for the ploughing of land which had been under grass for not less than three years ; to encourage general efficiency, there were to be grants for artificial insemination in beef herds, for grass drying, for the application of lime and phosphates. More vigorous use was to be made of the existing powers to develop marginal land, and more generous relief from income tax was given for expenditure on farm buildings, machinery and other equipment. Finally, it was hoped to secure some 100,000 new recruits to British agriculture, partly to replace the prisoners of war who were to be repatriated from 1947 onwards.

THE ACHIEVEMENT

Translated into acreages and livestock numbers, the targets set for 1951–2 appear as follows :

ACREAGES AND LIVESTOCK IN THE UNITED KINGDOM

	1936–8	1943	1947	1950	1951 Target *
Thousand Acres					
Wheat	1,856	3,464	2,163	2,479	2,630
Barley	929	1,786	2,060	1,779	2,250
Oats	2,403	3,680	3,308	3,105	3,350
Linseed	2	?	38	38	200
Potatoes	723	1,391	1,330	1,235	1,050
Sugar-beet	335	417	395	429	400
Other Crops	2,659	3,771	3,586	3,685	3,502
Total Tillage	8,907	14,509	12,880	12,751	13,382
Temporary Grass	4,145	4,219	5,651	5,605	5,230
Permanent Grass	18,750	12,330	12,404	12,770	12,400
Thousand Head					
Cows	3,280	3,550	3,540	3,767	3,712
Other Cattle	5,394	5,709	6,027	6,853	6,754
Ewes	10,807	8,201	7,143	8,072	8,460
Other Sheep (over 1 year)	3,126	3,416	3,363	3,677	3,080
Pigs	4,466	1,829	1,628	2,986	4,385
Poultry (million head)	76·2	50·7	70·0	96·1	129·0

* As revised in 1950

By 1950 the output of milk reached the target set for the next year and sales were virtually unrationed. The required number of other cattle and of sheep had also been attained, and the area under potatoes and sugar-beet was consistently higher than the target. But there was a marked shortfall in the area under grain, which was only partially offset by the higher yields obtained by improved varieties and higher standards of cultivation. The deficiency in grain and the disappointing level of imported supplies were together responsible for the failure of pigs and poultry to attain the required numbers. And finally, the extra workers did not materialise in the numbers suggested. Between 1947 and 1950 an increase of 30,000-40,000 in the number of men regularly employed on farms was offset by an almost equal fall in the number of women, and by the loss of the prisoners of war not included in these statistics. 'Displaced persons,' Europeans deprived by the war of home, nationality and employment, were the principal source of recruits to British agriculture in these years, but even with their help the labour force did not reach the expanded total thought desirable.

The effect of the expansion programme was thus to arrest, but not to reverse, the post-war decline in the area under grain, to increase the output of milk and to raise to a lesser extent the numbers of sheep and cattle. In addition it undoubtedly led to a very large investment in capital equipment of all sorts. The mechanisation of farm processes continued ; the number of tractors on farms in Great Britain rose from 173,000 in 1944 to 332,000 in 1950, as the British agricultural engineering industry rapidly expanded after the war. The provisions of the Hill Farming Act induced substantial investment in the ' marginal ' land devoted to sheep farming and cattle rearing, which should eventually lead to a larger output.

Counting the Cost

But it was the financial side of the expansion programme which most called for thought. In order to obtain an increase in annual output by 1951-2 of £100 millions (valued at 1946-7 prices), the Government offered some £185-£195

millions extra in higher prices and subsidies. There could
be no better illustration of the fundamental fact of agricultural
production—the law of diminishing returns, which summarises
the universal experience that, after a point, greater output
can only be obtained from a given area of land at a rising
cost per unit.

If agricultural wages and other costs had remained unaltered over the five years, farmers would be receiving by
1951–2 some £185–£195 millions extra in gross receipts,
which they would use, according to this plan, to produce
an extra quantity of food valued at £100 millions. That extra
quantity of food produced at home would not, it should be
noted, necessarily imply an equal sum to be saved from our
bill for imported food. In 1947 the prices paid to British
farmers for cereals were roughly in line with those paid in
sterling for imported cereals, but prices for livestock products
were higher in this country than for the equivalent imported
product. If this relation were to persist until 1951–2, it
would mean that, in order to save say £90 millions a year
on imported foods, the British consumer-taxpayer would be
paying double that amount in higher prices to British agriculture, both on an equivalent volume of food and on the
previously existing output.

Now there are obvious reasons why we should grow at
home a higher proportion of food supplies than we did between
the wars, since we can no longer secure the same volume
of supplies at the same favourable prices, prices which were
indeed quite unreasonably low in the years of the depression.
In the decade from 1940 the rise in the world's population
much out-stripped the increase in the world's food production,
and exporting countries now consume more of their own
output. Consequently there has been (and is likely to be in
the future) a smaller volume of food available for export,
a greater demand for it, and therefore a higher level of prices,
higher both absolutely and in proportion to the prices for
manufactured goods whose output can be more easily expanded. In these circumstances the total cost of our food
will be smallest, and a minimum quantity made more secure,

by growing at home a considerably higher proportion than in the inter-war years.

That is the economic argument that lies behind the post-war decision to maintain agricultural production above the pre-war level. But the general validity of this argument does not release us from the need to judge frequently the comparative costs of securing still a little more or a little less from home resources. Such a calculation was of especial importance in 1947, when a crisis in our balance of payments (which could then be regarded as a temporary phenomenon substantially relieved by the devaluation of the pound in 1949) induced an agricultural expansion whose full results could only be realised in four or five years, and which would lead to permanent investment of resources in agriculture. Just because two or three years may elapse between planning and performance, large changes in production policy should not be made to suit every minor change in international trade ; yet we must beware of maintaining unchanged a policy which changing circumstances may have rendered more costly than some now feasible alternative. Available data indicate that at prices ruling between 1947 and 1949, the total cost of food supplies was raised by an intensified home production, though a greater security in supplies would be obtained as a counter-advantage. Yet in 1950 the rise in world prices for cereals outstripped the increase at home, so that, by 1951, the Ministry of Food was paying higher prices for imported than for home-grown grain. Such unforeseen changes inevitably perplex the planners.

A sudden expansion in one major industry may also have undesirable reactions on the community as a whole. The purpose of the agricultural expansion programme was to achieve higher output so that imports could be cut without a fall in consumption. If one effect of this expansion was to raise the general level of prices and costs, its purpose—to redress an adverse balance of trade—would be frustrated through the repercussions on the volume of exports. If farmers and landowners were to invest, as required of them, in buildings, fences, machinery and other equipment, if they were to employ more workers, then in the circumstances of 1947 these productive resources would have to be taken out of other employment. The transfer might be achieved by administrative action; by the denial of building licences in rural districts until men and bricks and cement could only find employment in building cow-sheds and houses for farm workers; by forbidding other industries to buy the steel required for agricultural tractors. If these administrative measures were not successful, then the increased agricultural income would be used in competition with other demands; and men and machinery and steel would be taken into agricultural use by the offer of higher wages and higher prices which would react at once on the costs of industries making for export.

What in fact happened? The evidence indicates that the necessary transfer of resources was effected by a combination of both methods; the administrative measures were not sufficiently drastic to enable agriculture to obtain what was needed without a substantial rise in prices. There were constant complaints from the agricultural community that it could not get the resources it required or could only obtain them at constantly rising prices. And, eighteen months after the expansion programme was launched, the minimum wage for farm workers was raised by 4s a week and at the end of 1950 by 6s to £5 a week. Each time corresponding adjustments were granted in agricultural prices, so that the aggregate net income of farmers was not appreciably diminished by the rise in their costs.

Of course this rise in prices and in wages at the end of the nineteen-forties was not confined to agriculture, nor can it be ascribed to the expansion of agriculture alone. Wages in farming rose, partly because the level of prices enabled farmers to pay substantially more than the minimum wages to most of their men; and partly because industrial wages rose over this period equally with farm wages, so that the gap between the two was never abolished for more than a few months. The weight of economic opinion confirmed that in these years it was the combined total of national investment—in agriculture, in house building, in factories for the export trades

—which exceeded the level of the resources which could be made available, and which thus led to the phenomena of rising wages, rising costs and rising prices. The inflation thus generated continued indeed beyond the end of the decade and led after 1950 to renewed pressure on our balance o payments with other countries.

Improvements in Efficiency

In asking for an increase in agricultural output from 1947, the Government relied on more than the provision of additional resources ; it hoped that some of the increase would be secured by the better use of the existing equipment and manpower, by a general rise in the efficiency of management. In this task many of the changes brought about by the war and by post-war legislation were of great assistance. As the Agricultural Improvement Council noted at the end of the decade :

' A younger generation of farmers has grown up which has benefited from the agricultural education carried out during the last 20 years. . . . The fixed prices for agricultural requirements and the guaranteed markets and prices for agricultural products reduced the farmer's chance of making a quick profit from mere astute buying and selling and greatly enhanced the importance of technical skill in the business of farming. It became possible for the first time for the farmer to calculate with reasonable accuracy the financial result of applying a new method. Simultaneously, the industry felt the impact of the county War Agricultural Executive Committees' technical development work, which pressed on every farmer the need to improve his efficiency in the national interest. . . . Thus the problem of how to persuade farmers to adopt better methods has been largely replaced by the study of how to get the results of scientific research to the farmers in the shortest possible time. Again, the task of ascertaining, from an industry which often showed little interest, the problems requiring investigation has become that of assessing priorities to the many demands made on the limited men and equipment available for agricultural research.'[1]

This educational impact of the War Committees may have been their most important bequest to British farming. As noted earlier, the peculiar combination within them of technical experts and unpaid volunteers from the farming community brought scientists into touch with practical farmers throughout the country, and both had benefited from the contact. There was during the war a marked improvement in the general standards of management, reflected in the greater purchase of lime and fertilisers, in higher crop yields, in the better use of grass. The administrative experience of the local officers alone made possible those grants for ' marginal production ' from which were later developed the more comprehensive grants in aid of capital equipment and land fertility on hill and upland farms.

The War Committees were formally dissolved in 1947 ; at once reconstructed, they kept a medley of functions besides those concerned with technical efficiency which passed to the National Agricultural Advisory Service. There were the various controls over farm requisites which were gradually relaxed as supplies increased, until at the end of the decade only concentrated feedingstuffs were still rationed. There were also some 300,000 acres of land farmed by the committees themselves in England and Wales, whose future was uncertain. There were the various contract services for farmers which had been developed by some committees to a huge business. In Scotland these machinery and labour services were organised directly from the Department of Agriculture, which retained a central control ; in England and Wales they had developed as the need arose, and in such forms as the individual committees thought best to meet the circumstances of their areas. The Ministry made valiant efforts to enforce some uniformity between committees in their financial records and in their charges, but pressure of work and shortage of staff triumphed over formal accountancy. At the end of

[1] *Agricultural Improvement Council for England and Wales, Second Report*, p. 3

the war the Ministry instituted a stricter control over these services, which were also investigated in 1949 by the Select Committee (of the House of Commons) on Estimates.

These services involved the taxpayer in a heavy loss each year, since the payments made by farmers covered only a proportion of the costs involved. But it was difficult to calculate what the total costs were or the extent of the annual loss, since hostels for the committee workers were often provided and maintained by the Ministry of Works, and their wages, when unemployed by farmers, were charged by some committees to the account of the Land Drainage Branch or to Lands in Possession Branch, where they could not be disentangled from other costs. Making what allowance was possible for these divergencies in accounting practices, the Select Committee calculated that there had been a loss of at least £7–£8 millions in 1948–9 on these workers whose numbers fell from 54,000 to 40,000 in the course of that year. The loss—the difference between the sums paid by farmers for these workers and their cost to the committees—thus amounted to some £3 per man per week, an extravagant subsidy for the provision of casual labour. The investigators concluded that this employment, though it contributed to food production, was a wasteful method of doing so, and recommended that these gangs should be rapidly reduced and the men placed in ordinary farm work.

The other contract services—tractor cultivations, field drainage, weed spraying, pest control—also involved a financial deficit, which varied greatly from one committee to another. Some of this loss was inevitable in the early years, when the committee officers were inexperienced and their workers often unskilled, while farmers could only be charged a cost calculated on a reasonable level of performance. But there was also a feeling that smaller farmers, or those on the poorer land, would cut their production if they were charged even the reasonable cost of the services provided. During the war these concealed subsidies might be justified by such an argument, but by 1948–9 most of these farmers were already entitled to grants in aid of most types of capital improvement,

EPILOGUE

At the end of the nineteen-forties British agriculture was still searching for that stability promised in the post-war legislation. The implied guarantee under successive price reviews of a total income to the farming community as an aggregate certainly increased technical efficiency, in so far as that depended on new machinery, new buildings and a quicker adoption of scientific discoveries. But is such a guarantee (not extended to any other section of the community) compatible with a stable level of costs, with that form of efficiency which depends on the zealous elimination of every source of waste on every farm? In an era of rapid technical progress, it would be unreasonable to expect complete stability of farm prices ; but the rise both in agricultural costs and in agricultural prices at the end of the decade cannot encourage that wise forethought which enables technical progress to be economically assimilated into current practice.

The nation that emerged from war into victorious poverty has required and received of its farmers a greater output, and has offered assistance, administrative and financial, to help them on a scale unimagined in the years before September 1939. But neither farmers nor any other section of the community can hope to escape from inefficiency and poverty unless the nation achieves a measure of stability in the general level of prices and of costs.

INDEX

PRINTED IN GREAT BRITAIN AT
THE PRESS OF THE PUBLISHERS